"In memory

of those who have suffered

and continue to live in fear"

Lauder Lass –
The horse who touched the hearts of many

by

Lauder Lass
and Judi Gunn

Published by Hooves, Paws and Hands
Scottish Borders

Printed by Meigle Colour Printers Ltd, Galashiels

E: lauderlass@btinternet.com

ISBN 978-0-9569107-0-7

All proceeds will be split between Alzheimer's Scotland, Mossburn Animal Centre, Lauder & Channelkirk Church, Lauder Lass's upkeep and other animals who have been as abused as Lauder Lass.

Contents

Forewords

There is a reason for things happening, fate has a peculiar way of putting things in places where they are needed or need to go. Lauder Lass, who wrote the book you are about to read, was put by fate into the hands of Judi Gunn who, I suspect, could be acknowledged as a co author. Only Judi with her expertise in body language and her endless patience could have brought this amazing horse back from the mental hell into which she had been driven by the cruelty and neglect that had been her lot before fate intervened. Why, we do not know, but Lass has things to teach and tell us as you will find out and Judi has the knowledge and compassion to interpret them. Read and be moved, read and learn, open your hearts to this amazing horse who, through her human communicator, has something to teach us all.

Juanita Wilson
Mossburn Animal Centre
Hightae, Lockerbie, Dumfries

Judi speaks of the "alternative method" she uses to cure animals and people of ailments – an "animals friendly" method – and is one that she continues to promote in her book *Lauder Lass – The horse who touched the hearts of many*. She has written the book in the hope that the world will be encouraged to become a kinder place for those with communication issues. Dressed in a casual woolly top, wide-brimmed hat, black leggings and boots, her petite frame belies the impact of her electric personality. Her effervescent energy as she studies you with her soft green eyes under her long windswept hair attests to her vivacity and dedication. "There is no difference," she says, "between humans and animals – apart from one thing. Humans have a voice box, and usually that's a disadvantage!"

"Let silence speak" is her motto, by which she means we are bound together in a common bond of instinct. The bond is the natural way we communicate – through body language. We are all part of the same family where speech, our extensive verbal dictionary, is often a hindrance, like interference or static. To treat problems, especially psychological ones where animals or humans might have been exposed to some form of maltreatment in the past, we need to go back to basics – body language. "You have to think how a mare would treat a foal, how a cow would treat her calf, how a bitch would treat her pup, how a cat would treat her kitten or how a swan would treat her cygnet." This is the basis of Judi's approach, where kindness, understanding and non-aggression counts.

Charles Muller, Diadem Books

"Reading Lauder Lass's story has been, by turns, deeply moving and an inspiration. It seems she can teach the rest of us as much as Jodie and her visitors have been teaching her – about patience and understanding, about listening and responding, about the importance of simply taking time. I trust Lauder Lass continues to go from strength to strength and look forward to meeting her myself."

Mary Crockett
Writer and editor

Acknowledgements

I would like to thank:

Lauder Lass's previous owner for allowing her to have a second chance at life.
The people of Lauder who have been so supportive of Lauder Lass since day one, and all her other supporters throughout Scotland, England and abroad.

Particular thanks to:
Susan Windram of *The Southern Reporter*
ITV's news programme *Lookaround*
Dougie Johnston, *Photography, Lauderdale*
and *The Lauderdale News*

With additional thanks to:
Elaine Stewart, Bill Hayley, Tom Brodie, Becky Leigh, Kate Oliphant, B.J. Gunn-Grieve, Sarah Ryan, Jenny Horsley, Donna Sheep, Roddie Aitchison, Evan Anderson, Rebecca Grieve, Josie Hall, Emma Hardie, and Bruce MacBride for amazing artwork.

Juanita Wilson of Mossburn Animal Centre	Ruth Stirling
Hanna Fawcett	The South of Scotland Radionics Group
The Winterbottom family	The Fawcett family
Jane and Duncan Lowe	Bill Currie
Pam Bowler	Peter Neilson and Nod
Angela Stokes-Monarch	Rev Frances Henderson
Graeme Donald	The Oliphant family
The Stapleton family	Ian McGown
Marjory and Jimmy McKenzie	Jim Jeffrey the blacksmith
Ian Stewart	Joan Richardson
Anthony Tucker	Norma Pym
Lesley Stone at Border's Talking Books	Stephen Bradd
Scott Emond at Meigle Colour Printers Ltd	Allan Grieve for all his patience
Mary Crockett writer and editor	All Lauder Lass's visitors

And last but, by far, not least
My late father, Tony Gunn
for all the support you gave me before, during and after Lauder Lass came into our care.
You have all inspired me to write this book.
Thank you

Artwork

Poetry

Julie Moir – Scottish Borders
Becky Leigh – Lauder
L.F. – Scottish Borders
Chloe & Helen Paterson – Edinburgh
Penny Ryan – New Zealand
B.J. Gunn-Grieve – Lauder
Judi Gunn – Lauder
Thoughts for Hooves, Paws and Hands

The horse who touched the hearts of many

" ... but who was too scared to be touched or spoken to."

Based on a true story

HOPE AND DREAM

Soulful eye of unshed tears
Head hung low - unvoiced fears.
The quiet voice, the tender hand
Soft, fresh grass of calm, safe land.
The bond of trust twixt man and beast
So cruelly broken for such as these.
Tethered, beaten, hurt neglected -
Beaten again if dared reacted.
Born to love and trust and friendship,
Who could cause such pain and hardship?
What hard heart could ere resist
Those whose patience could persist,
To hope and dream and daresay pray -
To trust again another day.

Written by
J. Moir, Galashiels

Chapter 1

My early years

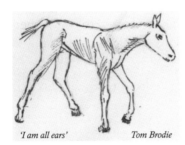

'I am all ears'   Tom Brodie

I WAS A CUTE dapple-grey Irish draught filly with big kind dark eyes and very long white eyelashes. My ears were perhaps a bit too big for my body, in fact I am sure people used to laugh at them, but I didn't mind about that. In fact, as time went on, I was very grateful because they were my alarm call when I sensed danger.

I grew a bit and still had my big kind-hearted dark eyes, but this time my legs were too long for the rest of my body. I'm sure everyone used to laugh at me because of them as well, but that was okay because as time went on they allowed me to run to break free.

I grew even more, still with my large loving eyes. I am sure I was almost bigger than my Mum (at least from what I can remember of her). My brief time with her gave me a sense of what it was like to be loved, and that feeling of belonging to someone was just tremendous. Oh, how often I wished for times like those early days as I grew older!

The next few years I had plenty of reasons to wish I had never grown up and was still next to my loving and protective Mum – but that wasn't to be. My bones ached, I was famished from the lack of food and water, I had scars and wounds all over me. My neck was cut – a four-inch indentation all the way round it can still be seen to this day. My muzzle was scarred from the number of times humans twitched me; my

ears were exhausted from having to be on duty 24/7, my brain and eyes (one of which, the left one, is damaged and enlarged from a clatter across the face) were exhausted with fear and anxiety at what the next moment might bring – shouting, brutish humans, dark long

draping coat, ropes, the chinking of chains, fires, screeching sounds from other animals, iron bars, gates, humans hitting me. But one of the things I was most frightened of was the dark, because this was when so much of the physical abuse I suffered took place. It was terrifying, but all this is not by far the worst that I had to contend with . . .
I often wonder what I ever did to the human race to deserve it all? Was it because I wasn't a beautiful thoroughbred or a stunning Welsh cob, or was it because of my big soft heart and my loving dark eyes with their long white eyelashes?

The first photograph in the middle of this book shows how bony I was, although it is not by any means the worst I have ever looked . . . My eyes are still big, but worried and filled with anxiety; my ears are totally out of proportion and my neck is hollow, my skin aches all over but particularly around my ribs, hips, chest, neck and muzzle. I think I looked a bit like a donkey – not that there is anything the matter with donkeys because I had a donkey friend many years ago and he was a wonderful buddy to have . . . He was almost a father to me, bless him.

Before I was brought to Scotland the humans who owned me starved me of food and water, herded me on a wagon, then a boat and more wagons and sent me across the water from Ireland. I was consistently abused and beaten with iron bars and other implements. I was petrified, cornered into a state where I had no option but to submit; chased by other horses to a point where I was scared of them too, even if they looked at me from a distance. If I tried to get away from the cruel humans I would be beaten and shouted at even more; my legs would be tied, I'd be given electric shocks, and have a four-inch collar tied round my neck and ropes put round

my knees (scars which can still be felt and seen today, ten years on). Not to mention being regularly dominated and restrained so they could control me while I was served by stallions – after which all of my five foals were taken from me at a very young age. I had no chance to develop my maternal instincts; and I fear only one of my foals may be alive today.

A MOTHER'S PAIN

Given no time
To know them well,
My children taken,
Me in Hell!
Love to give,
How shall I live?

I think of them often,
My heart sears with pain,
I know I will not
See them again.

Deep in my Soul,
Five little ones stay,
Forever loved – every day,
Sisters and brothers,
I am their Mother!

Written by visitor L.F.

I saw other horses being treated the same way. It was awful. I wished I could do something about it but I just didn't know how. Eventually one horrific incident, that I can't yet bear to talk about, made me decide I'd have to find some way to break free from this torture for ever. I tried to tell the other horses not to fight back because their lives would be made worse; some listened but some didn't and many of the latter never saw the next day. To say it was a nightmarish existence is nowhere near strong enough.

HELL

Aching head
Wish I was dead
They struck me hard
Out in the yard

Got no water
Got no food
Hell is here
Full of fear
He's coming back
I hear his tread
I'll warn him off by flicking my head
Then will kick
To see him dead!

Tied up..... ropes strain
Can't move
All is pain,
Beaten again
Blood runs
Legs won't hold
Sinking down
Where's my FOAL?
Cuts to my soul
Took him away
Hellish day

Dead of night
Daren't sleep
Ache all over
Bruises deep
Despair and pain
Tomorrow for me
Please Dear Lord
SET ME FREE

Written by L.F. Scottish Borders

After so many years of absolute turmoil, I desperately needed to think of a way so that no human could ever handle me again. From experience – and with the scars to prove it – I knew running would make the whole thing worse. I had tried to break free in the past, only to be beaten or tied down even harder, so I knew I really had to have a couple of plans and that I would have to pick the right moment. In the meantime, I had no option but to submit to all the things that were being inflicted on me. I often wished I were dead.

WAITING

Waiting for the day to come
When I can break free and run,
Why can't I be like those horses over there?
Their owners seem to care.

Written by
Becky Leigh, aged 11, Lauder

Chapter 2
I'm free and heading for Hob Nob's yard

'At last I am free' Bruce MacBride   *'Yippee' Evan Anderson*

EVENTUALLY, THAT OFTEN dreamt-of moment came. Something just snapped in me – no way was I going to let anyone touch me ever again! I had thought about putting my plan into action for years but had never really believed I'd be able to do it. Now, at long last, I had managed it. I was free! I just hoped my plan would work – that they'd never be able to catch me – otherwise I couldn't think what they might do to me. In fact, I don't know what else anyone could have done to try and break the little spirit I had left. I just felt that I had somehow to help the others who were being abused and will continue to be abused and shouted at until a stop is put to it. If you like, I was, and am, on a mission.

My plan resulted in me being trapped and put on yet another wagon – I was no use to my owners if they couldn't control me. I had no idea what was ahead of me. If only I could have understood the noise that came out of human mouths I might have known whether to put up a fight or not! But the body language of the human I saw next seemed different so I allowed myself to go with what was being asked of me. I was adamant, though, that I was not going to be restrained, not in any way, shape or form. In the past, purely in self-defence and because humans hadn't learnt from the flick of an unhappy head, I had taught myself to use my front right hoof to warn people off and if they didn't listen to that, my hind legs would come into play too. I wouldn't hesitate to use either if put under any pressure at all.

I was trundled on a two-hour journey to Scotland, where I was taken off and put straight into a stable. I wasn't given the chance to see any skylines to check if I could make out some form of a landmark to home in on. But what a luxurious stable, I thought, when I reached my destination! It was filled with straw, with feed in one corner and haylage stuffed full in a hay heck at the back; and there was fresh water in a bucket just inside the door.

THE RESCUE

Still full of fear,
But ... I like it here!
I have water and hay,
Kindness every day!

Stay on my guard!
Soon it will start,
What lies ahead?
Will I be dead?

Written by L.F, Scottish Borders

Although I had never been in this place before, some of the smells were familiar: wet, soggy mud, horse dung. One I didn't like that wafted over occasionally was the smell of smoke – burning wood, paper and plastic. If the wind was coming from a different direction there would be the most suffocating smell of burning coal. I recognised this one and tried desperately hard to blank out the horrible memories it triggered of my black days. Sometimes this was so difficult that even trying hard to think of the happy times standing and frolicking around with my wonderful Mum wouldn't work, but that's probably because those tender loving days seemed like a hundred years ago. It was very difficult to truly hold on to a positive feeling, even just for a few moments.

With having few other happy memories to latch on to I would take myself off into a corner and stand feeling dejected, rejected and lost, until something like a happy whinny, of a particular pitch, from a neighbouring horse would snap me out of it. But then I would wonder why they were so happy, and would desperately wish that, one day, I could neigh like them, with the same feeling of 'aren't I happy to be alive!' and 'isn't it a wonderful feeling, being cared for and loved!', instead of whinnying out of anxiety – and I couldn't even do that because I was sure I would be reprimanded somehow. *It's being able to think of positive things that has kept me going and I guess I'll just have to keep on dreaming with the tiniest ray of hope that things will come right for me in the end.* Even if I could have just a few genuinely happy days before I have to leave this, what seems to me, cruel, cruel world! I will continue to live in hope.

Outside this stable door was a long corridor and at the far side of it there was a big barn. I could smell other horses in the stables next to mine, and at night more horses were brought into the barn. I was relieved to see none of the animals here as stressed as the horses I had known in my life until then.

There was a young lady with a lovely smile and what seemed like a big heart who would visit me in my stable. She would try and give me Hobnobs and spend time later in the evenings standing perfectly still in the hope, I think, that I might take something from her hand. After a few weeks I allowed my guard down a bit but my instinct was still not to trust. If she came too close I would jump back as if I had had an electric shock again – flashbacks to the past would override my wish for a biscuit. When I was herded into the barn she tried working on me again but I was so fearful I would run – or even jump the six-foot wall to get away.

Most nights, this young lady would come to visit and sometimes an older lady would come with her; I think she might have been the young lady's mother. I think they both had a soft spot for me! But a few weeks in and I still couldn't overcome my defensive instinct. They tried a few things with me in the hope I could be handled but I just couldn't let my guard down, not after all these years of being dominated and abused. They tried so hard in their own way but I wasn't going to give up my recently found freedom. I was determined to escape if need be – I couldn't allow myself to be beaten again.

I kept to my plan, which had worked since the day I had first been given the chance to use it. It seemed to me that this was the only way to avoid having nasty things done to me; I saw no reason why I should change and risk being given the same kind of abuse. I will never ever allow that to be done to me again and will do my very best to stop others from experiencing the same.

There were totally different sounds at this new place. There wasn't so much shouting, there weren't so many tall aggressive-looking humans, and the other horses seemed to neigh happily. I could hear horses' hooves – happy hooves instead of anxiously stepped hooves – and that excited me. I couldn't hear any horse shrieks like I used to hear, and there were none of the other horrible sounds or smells that connected me to my past – this was a different place, with happier people. I occasionally thought, 'Maybe I could let my guard down,' but I hadn't been shown enough of what I needed, to feel confident enough to do this.

The only happy sound I remember from one of the places I had been was children's laughter and this I could hear at this new place. In fact every time I heard a child coming towards my stable my ears pricked up with joy. Why did I find children so exciting? My memories were vague because of all the abuse I had had to contend with.

I responded particularly well to a little boy at this new place so perhaps at some stage in my past there was a boy that I connected well with; perhaps this subconscious memory was from the time when I was a foal, perhaps not. Whichever way, it all seems such a very long time ago.

Apart from the happy young lady with the Hobnobs, there were other people wandering around who seemed to spend time with other horses. Perhaps they belonged to them or perhaps they were hired out to them. Oh for the feeling of belonging! I would so love that, but has my fear of people gone too far, I wondered? Am I now beyond help? Or is this kind young lady going to help me through this next chapter in my life? More to the point, can I afford to let her? Will I get hurt again, will I be collared and grabbed when I am eating my tea, or will I be so starved of water that I will end up desperate for a drink and then be collared? I can't afford that torture again, so, for now I will stick to my plan –it has worked for me in the past, therefore my trust barrier will stay firmly down!

Another couple of weeks passed by and I still had a lovely bed to lie on with breakfast, haylage and fresh water being served regularly. At night the nice lady continued to come out and offer me Hobnobs – at last there was some consistency in my life! – but I was still apprehensive about taking a biscuit. I had a whole host of anxieties, but one very cold night, when a horse's sense of smell is at its most acute, the smell of the oats in the biscuits made them almost irresistible. I gingerly went over, but if the lady's finger moved or one of her muscles twinged I would fly back and forget all about the smell of the biscuit for a while. This was hard, especially on a freezing night when an extra biscuit or two would have been most welcome.

IF ONLY

I'm a big grey mare,
Whose body is filled with fright
If only life could be fair
With lots of love and light.

I'm so scared of the dark
and of every bark.
If only life could be fair
And show me some warmth and care.

Written by B.J, aged 7

The day-to-day routine here seemed to be: Lights on – this was a great relief because I was so scared of the dark – then my feed bucket from the night before would be removed, along with the buckets from my neighbouring stables. Eventually the kind lady (aka Hob Nob) would return with my bucket re-filled and a man would arrive with the hosepipe to fill up the water buckets. The horses from the barn were taken out – at this stage I wasn't sure where to, but I could always hear them, so they weren't that far away. More importantly, they weren't being hurt, which was such a relief to me. My neighbouring stable companions would go out or away for a wee while but would return by the end of the day, before dark.

To start with, once the other horses were out of the barn, I would be allowed in there to stretch my legs. It felt good, even though it was a bit dark. There were times in my past when I rarely saw the light, so I was pleased that I could always see the people walking up the corridor towards the hay shed at one end. At the other end, it smelt like the feed room, so I always kept an eye out, in the event that a bit of extra feed might come my way. But I still never allowed myself to go too close – just in case.

They would fill up a hay net or two and dangle them just over the six-foot corridor wall. A bit of time saw me gaining confidence to eat as the people walked by. Sometimes through the day the people were away but I would have the audible company of some puppies that were put in one of the stables until the others returned, so as such I was never on my own. The sun shone in the wee window at the back of my stable in the early afternoon, and I could hear other horses' hooves walking along what sounded like a solid road. They didn't sound like any of the steps that I knew from the horses I had met so far, so perhaps they lived somewhere else. My ears were alert all the time for any new or familiar noises like specific engines and car doors banging or the sound of the nice lady's voice.

If I was left in on my own and if no one was going around in the barn I would, in between munching my hay, watch all that was going on through my wee window. From here I could see something that looked like a small pond in the centre, and a metal box with windows and a wooden log house where the people came and went – it must be their stable! I could hear cars, tractors and dogs barking. So all in all this seemed an interesting, non-threatening place to be.

The barn was quite big, in fact big enough for me to run from one end to the other if I felt too threatened by humans. In the centre but three metres from one of the long sides of the barn were some old jumps stacked on top of each other, which the horses at night used to scratch against, usually resulting in an almighty clattering heap waking everyone from their evening doze!

Chapter 3
Hob Nob introduces Hat lady

'What are they up to?'

I MUST HAVE BEEN at Hob Nob's big yard for just under two months when one afternoon she brought another lady along. I had never met this new person before but I sensed something completely different about her. Although I was very curious, I was also wary, not knowing what was afoot. I pretended I didn't notice them talking in the corridor, but I sensed they were talking about me. They must have talked for a good 20 minutes before either of them moved. Whoever this new lady was, I decided to call her Hat lady because she was wearing a big brimmed hat!

I was quietly eating my haylage in the far corner of the barn when the gate bolt was opened and in walked the Hat person! Mmm, not sure of this one, I thought to myself. I watched out of the corner of my eye, so she'd think I wasn't looking at all. She had an armful of stuff! Mmm, what was she going to do with that, I wondered? She ignored me totally! That's extremely unusual, because most people come straight up to me, using what wouldn't be considered brisk body language to most horses but to me is like a wild cat chasing its prey; and it's at that stage I would normally back or run off before they came within 15 metres of me.

Hat lady still ignored me, keeping her back to me all the time and her eyes under her big brimmed hat. I'm sure she thought I was ignoring her, but I was watching every muscle that moved. She proceeded to lay her baggage down beside the jumps and stayed in the centre, motionless for about ten minutes. I couldn't see her eyes, which I wasn't sure to take as a threat or not, then she proceeded to walk, very slowly, round in little circles at the very bottom of the barn, still not either looking at me or bothering me in any way at all. How unusual! I have never seen this non-aggressive behaviour before. She gave out quite a few large vocal yawns and walked slowly, with no vicious-looking hand movements. I felt a wee bit safe, but confused. Never had I known a human to be so silent. I was used to words being spoken or shouted at me – this was very strange indeed. I kept thinking to myself, there's a con here, I am sure!

My large white ears were on red alert (sticking up like those of an Egyptian Pharaoh hound) and my eyes, although hidden under my long white forelock, were in alert mode all the time she was there. Mmm, what is she up to? How bizarre! But it was so nice not to be shouted at, chased or cornered.

As the minutes went on, with me still in alert mode, her circles were becoming larger, almost filling up the bottom half of the barn. She was getting closer to me, but still with no aggressive body language, so I thought I'd just pretend to eat and prepare myself to run just in case. She's on some form of mission, I am sure, I thought. No human has spent this amount of silent time with me.

A good half-hour later, she started to get closer. I stopped pretending to eat and raised my head a bit. She had her back to me, which wasn't too bad, but as soon as she got to about ten metres away it was too close for comfort and I ran bucking and rearing, creating a whirlwind of dust behind me as I galloped to the furthest point the arena would allow me. She backed off slightly. I went round at least twice and as I was coming up towards the top end I wasn't having any more of this. I got ready to jump the wall beside the corridor (this I had done before). But as soon as she saw this change in me, she immediately reversed back to the centre and sat down with her head bowed. After running another couple of circuits I realised she wasn't a threat after all, so I slowed down to a trot and eventually to a walk and stopped at my haylage pile. I was trying to say to her, I just want to eat, leave me alone. Hat lady remained totally stationary in the middle for a while and then started the same thing again.

Everything was silent, apart from the odd bird song, as she reversed up to me again. I reacted just as before, but as soon as I got to the point where I was thinking about jumping the wall, she reversed back. I still felt pushed, so I kept running, swishing my tail and flicking my neck to tell her I was unhappy about the pressure she was putting on me. Each time I got to the point where I had initially thought about jumping she reversed back to take the pressure off. Well, never had I experienced this type of language before, someone who responded to my silent request. This was something else! No shouting whatsoever, just the sound of yawns and bird song.

After 15 minutes of anxiously cavorting around (on my part) I was almost quite enjoying it. I started to raise my tail a bit with pride and stretched my trot to an extended trot. I felt good and I think I looked stunning! When Hat lady bowed down I began to realise that I could slow down; when she slowly got up again I started to walk. For the first time, we had a two-way communication going – it was sweatingly awesome. But my internal alarm still dictated that no one was to come any closer than ten metres.

We kept working like this for a while, me stopping as she stopped and she stopping when I stopped. It was just tremendous. Perhaps at long last I have found someone who will give me what I need to make me a normal horse! But, oh no, she suddenly scratched her head! That freaked me, I galloped off, threatening to jump the wall again. As soon as she saw the change in my body language, though, she reversed as fast as she could, almost as if to say she was sorry. It was odd, so odd. Never had I had a human apologising to me before!

Once I had calmed down we started from scratch again. I began to realise each time I BLIPPED we would have to start from scratch. As you can imagine, this happened quite a number of times on this first day (she was with me for about two hours, I guess) and indeed quite a few days after that. Hat lady was cunningly clever, though. She made me calmly stop each time away from my haylage! But the last half-hour of each session saw us standing relaxed/exhausted and still, ten metres away from each other but AWAY FROM MY HAY!!!

At the end of the first session I was a bit like a sweat rag because my brain had HAD to work on a completely different communication level than it ever had before. I felt truly exhausted at the end, but it was a positive feeling because I did not get hurt. Hat lady didn't threaten or shout at me like most people had done in the past, nor did she have any whips or sticks or long pieces of metal to hit me with.

Then, after each last half-hour of peace she would disappear! Would she ever come back, I thought to myself? Had she disappeared for ever? I so hoped not, because she was about the only one who seemed to understand how scared I was of interacting with humans. After she left the barn I decided to smell every footstep she had taken, just as I would if I had been a normal horse and another horse had entered my stable! Or as a dog would do had another dog gone into its home or garden.

That evening I was herded back to my stable so that the other horses could come in for the night. I didn't stop thinking about my first experience with the Hat lady until I heard the clattering of feed buckets! Mmm, tea and fresh water – how I love fresh water! – so for an hour or so I just concentrated hard on eating my tea and haylage, and taking deep, refreshing gulps from my water bucket.

My body felt sticky and itchy after all that sweating so I needed a scratching post. I found just the thing, a sharp corner, ah, wonderful – then WHOLLOP! Out of fright I jumped into the opposite corner of my stable, only to discover that my neighbouring horse didn't like me rubbing, or perhaps it was the noise I was making while I was doing it? Whichever way, I learnt that if I needed a scratch I should make sure that my neighbour was out first! I plucked up the courage to take a wee bit of a Hobnob from the nice lady that feeds me and for the first time I lay down in my stable and slept like a baby.

I didn't see the Hat lady for a couple of days, possibly because she knew my first session had exhausted me, or perhaps the Hobnob lady had told her that I was tired out. However it was, the Hat lady must have told my owner how to approach me, because her behaviour seemed to change towards me. It made me feel a bit easier and less threatened.

I found myself thinking a lot about the Hat lady and her 'me friendly' ways and began to wonder whether her visit was just one of those never-again sessions. However, I still got some wonderfully fresh water, tasty haylage and a food mix, not forgetting my night-time Hobnobs. The only thing I continued to really dislike or be frightened of was total darkness. When the evening light faded and silence drew in I hated it, and the sudden movements of humans. Having the other horses around made me feel more secure – and dogs barking had always been a warning sign for me, so as long as they didn't bark I felt a little bit safe.

At times my new owner tried hard to stroke me but I found this still difficult and scary. What with the straw on my stable floor irritating on my fetlocks (ankles), there were times when I would stamp the floor with my hind (back) leg. This would make my owner jump, so then I would jump because she had had a fright – a kind of roll-on effect. Or was it my long, dirty white tail tickling my fetlocks? I wasn't sure, because I had never had a short tail to feel the difference. The other thing was – not that it was intentional – but if she suddenly scratched her head or moved the hand that she wasn't stroking me with, I would jump with fear that I was going to be beaten up again. Also, she sometimes wore very noisy waterproof trousers and they scared me too. On those days I am afraid I wasn't very happy to accept any kind of treat or stroke from her. I guess with the weather sounding so horrible outside she probably needed the trousers to keep her dry, but I was scared of the crunchy noise they made.

Through the day I heard various things: footsteps, different cars and dogs barking, a peacock squawking and a very odd duck quacking, all of which I became quite used to, and then of course there were the regular voices. I became familiar with them, just as I got used to the daily routine of the yard. Sometimes I would hear what sounded like a big lorry starting up. I quivered the first few times I heard this, because I was frightened it meant I would be going on yet another trip. But the only thing that followed on from the lorry starting up was that my Hobnob owner would disappear! I guess she must have had to go away every so often. I didn't like it when she wasn't around because someone else looked after us all and it just wasn't the same at all.

Chapter 4
Hat lady returns

'Oh no, it's Hat lady?'

DURING ONE OF THE times when Hob Nob wasn't there I heard the sound of a car I hadn't heard for a while, then a gentle bang of the door closing. I thought I recognised the voice talking but couldn't quite connect it with anyone; then I heard footsteps coming towards the entrance of the stables. I stopped eating the haylage in front of me and pricked up my big white ears – it was the Hat lady. Then it suddenly dawned on me why I couldn't quite recognise her voice – she didn't speak when she was working with me the last time. Well, I was kind of pleased to see her but on the other hand I was a bit unsure, because her way of communicating was foreign to me. There was nothing horrible about her; I could sense that – and there was no ulterior motive in what she was sharing with me.

Like the last time, she took her coat and bag into the centre of the barn and sat on one of the jumps with hat on head. She didn't look at me or anything; I still didn't know quite what to make of this but she did the same thing last time so I kind of went back to eating with, unbeknown to her (I thought!) one of my big dark eyes on her at all times. There was no one else around at this time so it was very peaceful with just Hat lady and me, oh and the birds singing in the background.

At least, it was peaceful until there came an almighty sound like elephants trumpeting. I immediately raised to attention and grew at least two feet taller, snorted and pranced until Hat lady moved her hand and all of a sudden it stopped! By jings, I had never heard that one before – a totally new sound to go into my memory bank! After a few moments I relaxed and wandered back to my net filled with haylage, but just at that moment Hat lady got up and started to walk round the bottom of the barn, like the last time. Her circles got bigger, then she started to walk up and round the circumference of the barn – mmm, she's

15

coming a bit too close for my liking – but she stopped about 15 metres away. Not that I was staying where I was – I started to walk towards the bottom corner. Well, blow me, she proceeded to go towards my haylage and took the lot away! How dare she do that? It was mine, all mine! I was quite unimpressed so I let out an almighty snort.

A few moments passed while she was raking up the last strands of haylage. Everything about how she moved was slow and calm so I didn't feel too anxious, although I have to admit I was a bit dischuffed – especially after all those years of little food and water. Hat lady then walked back to the centre, about 17 metres away from me, still without looking at me. She stopped for a few moments, lifted the elephant thing up and put it back down again and then my work was cut out!

She turned round with her belly button being in line with my shoulder – I was off as fast as the speed of sound, you couldn't see me for dust! I ran round that barn as fast as I could, getting myself into a real state – the steam from my back was making its own tramline in line with the dust being kicked up by my hooves. I was going so fast I couldn't even see her; then I thought, 'what am I doing? There's nothing chasing me and I can't even see what the Hat lady is doing!' So I slowed down a bit, trying to see where she was, but because of the speed I was going I couldn't see anything for dust. I stopped where I felt safe, in other words where my haylage had been – at least until SHE had moved it. I was expecting to see her standing where I had seen her last but she wasn't, she was sitting cross-legged on the stained sawdust floor with her back to me! I was thoroughly confused and didn't know what to make of all this at all. What had I wasted all that energy for? And how come her back was turned to me?

Hat lady rose again, but very slowly. I guessed this was because I'd gone dashing off like that. As her back was still turned I thought I would try and devour any strand of haylage that she might have missed or not seen, but no, she had picked up the whole dashed lot. What a miserable human being!

Hat lady turned round; I couldn't see her eyes at all, just the rim of her hat. She started to walk towards 3 o'clock, (I was at 10 o'clock), her hands steady and by her side. Her walk was not at all aggressive or with intent to harm, but I stuck to my guns to protect myself and did not go anywhere near her. Then she started to head up towards 1 o'clock. 'She's going in my direction, I'm out of here!' I thought. As soon as I cantered off, though, she sat down. I kept cantering till I had run three-quarters the length of the arena, but she hadn't moved so I slowed down and stopped at my security blanket corner (aka the haylage corner). She got up again and took a pace forward; I ran again. She crouched down; I stopped. Mmm, a definite pattern: she gets up, I run; she sits down, I stop; she gets up and I run; she gets up and walks towards me … I run for my life!

This pattern went on for about ten minutes then everything changed because the next time she started to rise and noticed I was just about to run for my life, she only half-rose.

This was enough to encourage me to go forward, but in walking mode not 'run for your life' mode.

We did the same thing numerous times until I had got the hang of it. As I was gaining confidence, she rose totally and lo and behold I just walked away and didn't run for my life! It was awesome: someone who was trying to work with me instead of against me all the time. It took a lot of brainwork though, but a different type of brainwork from what I had had to use before. I think Hat lady sensed I was tiring a bit so she left the barn. Although I was tired I was hoping that she would come back, because there was a little bit of me that enjoyed this new form of interaction. Perhaps she left intentionally so that I would think about my latest lesson! But two minutes later she returned with a wee drop of haylage – aw, that was nice of her, I thought. But I wasn't about to go near the pile until she was at a very safe distance away or totally out of the barn. As it happened, she left the barn. Mmm, it was so nice to have something to eat after all that hard work! But you know, as I was eating away I was also thinking, for the first time ever, that I'd like her to come back and stay with me while I was eating. Well, just a second later she did come back, this time with a box that she proceeded to sit on. Maybe Hat lady can read my mind, I thought – how awesome that would be, if someone truly understood me! We stayed in our corners for another ten minutes – just enough time for me to regain my energy.

After this ten-minute break Hat lady got up and started to move the jumps around. She didn't create a jump or anything, but she quietly and gently laid two long poles out, lengthwise, with a big gap in the middle. I think she created this to jump over herself because she tried them out about six times. A human horse-jump course!

After completing the jump poles she walked round her creation for a while, almost as if she was showing me what to do from a distance; and then, instead of staying in the centre, she slowly moved to the opposite corner to where I was. Mmm! What's she up to now, I wondered. She started to walk very slowly towards me, but backwards! Mmm, not sure of this one, but Hat lady was very responsive in that if I moved a muscle she would crouch down a bit as if to say, it's okay, you don't have to run. It must have taken her about 15 minutes to walk backwards up to me – stopping at a safe distance away, about 12 metres – until I suddenly realised what she was asking me to do. She wanted me to turn the other way. Ah ha, so that's what she wanted! Okay, that was fairly easy and not scary. I'll accommodate that one again, as long as Hat lady's requests are as slow as that and not what I would consider threatening.

I continued to walk round calmly until I came to the two poles placed at each side. I'd been trapped enough in my day, so no way was I going to be trapped again. I quickly dodged them by doing a flying leap to the right – and went back to walking round the very edge of the arena. Hat lady started to walk a bit faster and blocked the opposite corner to the one I was approaching. There was no way I was heading in her direction so I about-turned and went back the way I had come, which meant passing the poles again! I thought I was being a clever cookie by side-jumping them, but Hat lady ran this time to the top furthest away corner, which made me turn in the opposite direction again. This time, though she was walking closer to me, probably about nine metres away but parallel with me, her hands still by her side but her legs walking with me. I really wanted to dodge the poles again but she kind of made me go through them because of the distance between us. I truly did not want to do this so I broke into a gallop as I passed through them, so that the poles couldn't jump up and hurt me. As soon as I went through, though, Hat lady crouched down quickly as if to say, there's no pressure, you can slow down.

I truly amazed myself and thought, 'That wasn't too bad at all and there was no con!' Hat lady wanted me to do it again, so this time I decided if I was to start trotting I'd beat her to the poles and be able to dodge them, but as I trotted she trotted, which made me run faster; but as I ran faster she ran faster to the point where I was concentrating so much on what Hat lady was doing that I went through the poles without even thinking about it! Wow, that was okay. After I'd gone through them she crouched down again, which made me slow down and stop about 15 paces later. She didn't look at me at all but stood motionless for a few moments, perhaps just to let me think about what I had just done. I shook my head in a positive way, to show her that it was okay actually.

Hat lady gave me a moment of stillness then walked back to the poles to change them. This time she straddled an extra five-inch pole across the two side ones so that it was like a single trotting pole. She gave it a shake to make sure it was tight, walked about six paces away from the cross pole then started to jog herself and then jumped it and continued on for a further six steps, turned about and repeated the process! 'She likes to keep fit!,' I thought to myself. I watched every move she made, with a little more curiosity than fear. She walked back to the centre and encouraged me to walk on quietly. If I jogged she would crouch down, which would bring me back to a walk. Then, when I eventually got to about ten metres from the pole and I tried so hard to dodge, Hat lady's body language wouldn't let me – so I jumped for the world. It felt as if I had jumped the Eiffel tower! I completely surprised myself but, more to the point, I found my tail up high and I was carrying my head in a totally different position. *For the first time I had found something that was or could potentially be good fun and I had shared it with someone without being scared or hurt. What a feeling! It was just tremendous.* I so wanted to do it again so I kept going. Hat lady retreated but stayed parallel with me, although this time I gauged the distance and stretched my legs out as far as I could. It was just awesome – it could have been the River Nile I had just jumped.

As I continued to trot after jumping the jump, Hat lady crouched down again. This was my cue to slow down, so I did as I was asked. This time she walked back to the jump and removed it. I was gutted, I so wanted to do more. But I guess she had my best interests at heart – after all, I was pretty skinny and unfit, ungroomed, dirty, with knots in my mane and hooves that looked a bit like a pair of pauper's shoes, all covered with unhealthy lines and with cracked or rough edges – a little like a ragged bit of slate from a rooftop.

I so enjoyed this day, my first for a long, long time. It was truly wonderful to be asked to do something freely. I was beginning to enjoy Hat lady and hoped that she would stay in my life.

To end this session she encouraged me to walk round slowly, I guess so that I could cool off after being so excited. I started to walk as did she, but instead of having her belly to my shoulder pushing me on, she was walking slowly with me, with her head going the same way as mine and half a foot behind my shoulder although still ten metres away from me. It was so comforting to have someone walking *with* me, albeit not right next to me. I couldn't have coped with that! We must have walked round together for about ten times, stopping intermittently for a breather and to change direction to go the other way. But the loveliest thing was, we both stood totally still, parallel to each other, for about 15 minutes before the session finished

Today with Hat lady felt good. I had learned how to be turned around in a totally non-threatening way; I realised I could jump out of enjoyment instead of having to jump to escape from pain and abuse. But more to the point, I could sense a connection with Hat lady. It was all just so much to take in, though, on top of all my thousands of bad memories with humans. Was all this too good to be true? Time would tell, but in the meantime I could not let a total of five hours rule out all those negative years behind me.

I think we were both tired that night and I know I slept like a log; but before my eyes closed for the night I can remember saying to myself, 'I hope Hat lady will come back.' I didn't even hear my owner coming in with my lovely smelling oaty Hobnobs, so I guess I must have been shattered. In fact I believe she came in and saw me lying down for the first time. I always tried not to be sleeping when I heard voices, because of the fear of being hurt.

Chapter 5

For the first time I feel a hint of being understood

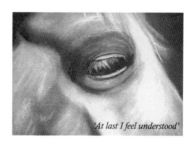

'At last I feel understood'

FOR THE NEXT FEW days I was very tired, but not from the amount of work I had done with Hat lady. *It was from the emotion of knowing that someone had shown me an individual can be understood no matter what the circumstance* and that perhaps, just perhaps, there was a chance that I could begin to relax for the first time in an extremely long time.

It was as if a wee bit of the weight had been taken off my tall, thin, scrawny shoulders for a moment – an extremely positive feeling of exhaustion. Upon my owner's return she commented on how much more relaxed I seemed. In fact I even let her touch my off side (my right side) for the next few nights – until she made a wrong move and I backed off with fright, the memories that had receded slightly streaming back with a vengeance, leaving me feeling insecure again and the positive moments with the Hat lady thrown into utter oblivion!

The next few days I was back to feeling the way I was on my first day with Hob Nob – but then I heard the gentle sound of that car door shutting. I so hoped it was Hat lady and what a relief it was to hear her cough. She had coughed from time to time through my previous sessions and now, for the first time, I think she noticed my ears prick up with happiness. I was so eager for her to come into the barn that I stopped eating the little bit of haylage I had left. Out of excitement! I could feel my heart rate rise and my blinking became faster. I so needed Hat lady to give me some more of the positive feeling she had managed to give me before.

As soon as she entered the barn I was up and ready for work and willing to comply with whatever would be asked of me – as long as she didn't come too close to my body, but especially my face, head and neck. So when she asked me to go round the arena a few times, I went round as good as a wee lamb, even when she silently asked me to change direction from the opposite side of the barn.

As Hat lady worked with me she remained calm and silent. After a wee while she went away to set up a small jump, only about a foot high. Yippee, I thought to myself – I loved the free jumping I did the other day. So, as a thank-you for the previous session if nothing else, I felt I should show her what I was made of. We worked well together until someone walked straight into the barn – but Hat lady kindly suggested that the new person went back out for a minute or two. I was wary until they were completely out and the bolt had been securely shut. Hat lady encouraged me to walk on but as soon as I got to the barn gate where the new person was standing I took a wide berth so that I was far enough away not to be hurt. What I hadn't realised as I was dodging the door was that I had flown past Hat lady and was only two metres away from her, and you know, starting up, she didn't hurt me! I completely surprised myself; perhaps I could let my trust barrier come down a bit further with Hat lady . I think I feel safe when she is with me.

As much as I had hoped I wouldn't have to go past the bolted gate again, Hat lady encouraged me on and over the jump. I was all prepared to give the gate a wide berth again when all of a sudden Hat lady moved three paces closer to me, but still in line with my shoulder. She was still about three metres away – far enough for me to feel pushed – so I had no option but to go past the bolted gate. I picked up speed just before it, though, and zapped past it as fast as I could, starting up; but just as I passed her, Hat lady crouched down. Well, I wasn't going to slow down for her till I felt I was far enough away from the new person standing at the other side of the gate. After a few moments this person said, 'I can see you are busy, so I'll catch you later, Jodie.' Ah ha, so that's Hat lady's name! Jodie, I'll try and remember her as Jodie instead of Hat lady from now on.

I was popped over the jumps a few times, which truly delighted me – I had found something I really enjoyed doing, apart from trying to understand Jodie's way of communicating, that is.

She turned her back to me and walked away towards the jump. Mmm, she's not looking, I could maybe go and eat the remnants of my hay, I thought. So I crept off while she removed the jump. Aw, I liked doing that, I thought, but I guess she had her reasoning! She started to walk back towards me but stopping about ten feet away from me. As she saw my muscles starting to move she slowed down until I started to walk on. Jodie's body language had changed, though, and I couldn't understand why – perhaps she was going to try and introduce something new? I react badly to new things, especially if I feel there is even the tiniest hint of a threat to me.

As I was walking round she was kind of walking sideaways, in line with my shoulder, encouraging me on for a further three or four laps. Then she crouched down, so I slowed down and came to a stop about eight paces further on. Her body language

21

changed again. This time she was heading in the same direction as me, in line with my body. We both stood still, parallel with each other; arms, head and legs completely. It was just awesome starting up, standing next to, albeit three metres away, someone who wasn't threatening me. I could feel my head lowering, my eyes almost wanting to sleep and my off hind leg (my back right leg) desperately wanting to rest; but I just couldn't let myself go. Once Jodie had sensed I was relaxed she took a step sideways towards me with the rest of her body motionless; I could handle that. Then she took another step sideways. I lifted my head a little, to show her that I was ready to run if she made one wrong move, but she waited till I lowered my head again and then took another step towards me. That was one step too close for my liking, however, so I galloped off with a swish of my tail.

She followed me half-way round the barn and then gently walked across to the opposite corner to block me or to make me slow down to stop. We must have repeated this process at least six or seven times, but I wouldn't let her get any closer than two-and-a-half metres away. I think she felt that I had done well to get to that stage, so she rewarded me by putting the jump up again. I loved this and so wanted to do more, but she stopped me short and proceeded to follow me like a shadow – courteously staying four metres away, to start with anyway. At times she would be directly behind my tail, so with not being able to see what she was up to I would change direction so that I could see her from the side of my eye. Well, she must have followed me in this way for about 20 minutes. It suddenly dawned on me that it wasn't me that was choosing to turn but Jodie, who was asking me to turn by moving to a spot where she knew I couldn't see her. I still wasn't going to let her get too close to me. 'This lady is a clever cookie,' I thought to myself. She was far too clever in fact. She managed to make me turn about every five paces, which meant we were only using a quarter of the arena. Then she changed everything and started to block me again to make me stand still so that she could stand parallel with me. I knew this one from before, and there was still no way I was going to let her get closer to me, no matter how motionless or how long it took. She tried so hard to come closer but my system said NO!

I think she was still quite proud of what I had achieved, though, because she rewarded me with another ten minutes of jumping. It was just awesome being rewarded in this way for the positive steps I had taken, *instead of being bribed with a bucket of feed dangled in front of me so that I could be roped and controlled*. The only thing I asked myself was: why did she always stop short of the thing I enjoyed doing the most? Was it because she felt I would become too tired too quickly, being so unfit, or was it so that it would leave jumping as a fun thing to do or so that I wouldn't become bored of my reward? Whichever way, *it was a lovely experience being able to share these moments with someone who was trying to understand me for what I am and not for what people expected of me as a member of the equine world.* But my underlying thought was always, 'When's the bad bit coming? I must not let my guard down.'

For the last 20 minutes of this session we did as before – stood next to each other, albeit with a distance between us, but perhaps a foot closer. Then she reversed back towards the centre and picked up her bits and pieces and slowly left the arena. Same thought: will she come back?

I was very tired again after this session so it was another few days before I saw Jodie again, but the daily routine kept me occupied. The outside world had turned snow white, which made the blackness of night-time more a gorgeous colour of purple. I often gazed out of my wee stable window, daydreaming, watching the morning sunrises – they were just awesome. It was so nice not to have the horrible old familiar sounds of clattering rail tracks, cars and lorries and buzzing pylons and the suffocating smells of coal, burning plastic and fumes from cars and wagons. The air seemed fresh; it was wonderful. I was beginning to like the peace.

Jodie returned a few days later but this time she came in with Hob Nob. Mmm, I thought: what are they doing in here together? I was quite happy with just one person working on me, thank you very much. I don't do two people at a time! I pricked my ears up and listened to the tones of their voices. They had a plan, I could tell. I don't like human plans – I have seen too many of them in my past. I was up and ready from the moment they came in – at least until Jodie suggested to Hob Nob that it would be better if she sat down.

As Jodie was working me I came down off my high horse a bit, but I still sensed that something was up, and sure enough, a wee while later she stopped me, by her usual crouching down. Hob Nob walked slowly up to the top corner of the barn but about six metres away from the wall. Mmm, I can easily dodge her, I thought to myself. Jodie started to make me walk but as I reached the corner before where Hob Nob was, I grew a bit – no way was I going to be encouraged to go past her. I picked up speed and fled past her as fast as the speed of light, but on the inside of the arena. I slowed down when I felt safe, which was by the time I had got to the bottom corner. Jodie, from about ten metres away, continued to encourage me round, but this time her body language changed to the point where she was almost pushing me out. Well, if they thought for one minute I was going to be cornered, possibly grabbed and caught, then they had another think coming! So I went hell for leather past Hob Nob, but this time in between the corner and her. 'That was a bit too clever, Jodie,' I thought. 'I can see I am going to have to try and mind-read you a bit better.'

I was pushed gently round like this for at least another ten circuits or perhaps it was until my body showed less fear of doing what was being asked of me. Hob Nob hadn't moved a muscle; maybe they weren't going to corner me after all. Gradually I was encouraged to slow down, closer and closer to Hob Nob, until I had gained enough confidence to stop about four metres away from her, but only about five minutes Hob Nob twitched and I was off. I almost wished I hadn't, though, because the whole process was repeated until I was stationary again. Mmm, I see, I thought, if I don't do something that's asked of me, they repeat it until I do. Okay, I'll see if I can pluck up the nerve to be braver. They aren't hurting me, after all.

Over a period I would be asked to walk past and to stop beside Hob Nob. It was okay, actually, at least until Hob Nob moved. I think I heard her mention the words 'cramp in my leg', although I don't know what this means. Once I had realised that I wasn't going to be eaten up and spat out, I walked past and stopped with ease and I guess I kind of got used to Hob Nob's cramp twinges and to Jodie guiding in her kind and gentle way.

As this day went on, the only thing I wouldn't allow was for Hob Nob to touch me. I'd stand about a metre away but nothing else – touching me, well, that was completely taboo! Eventually Hob Nob quietly retreated and the session drew to a close, but before it ended I was given my favourite reward to date – another little jumping session. It was wonderful to feel my mane and tail flowing so happily again – another learning session with a positive result.

Jodie returned a few days later and continued working along similar lines as before: working from behind, stopping and starting me, walking quietly up to me, but I couldn't cope with the latter. So, part way through this session she shrunk the size of the arena, using a thick white tape. Little did she appreciate that I would bolt in such a small or confined area! Oh dear, I think I did the wrong thing. But she did take down the white tape, so obviously I managed to get my message across. She seemed disappointed but continued to work with me for a period. I didn't get my reward at the end, though.

Chapter 6

Feeling rejected yet again!

'What's to become of me?'

ALL OF A SUDDEN the elephant sound happened again, but I wasn't too fazed by it because I had heard it going off a few times before. Jodie put her hand in her pocket and pulled out the little black thing, pressed a button and it stopped, then she moved to the centre of the arena and sat on a jump.

I quietly walked with her and stopped about six metres away, but it seemed as if she was suddenly under pressure. Her body language had changed; she rested her head on a hand and looked sideways at me. All in all, she looked a bit like a limp horse rug hanging on a wall or like I often felt when I felt rejected, dejected and lost. She seemed weary and concerned but I couldn't work out why. Had I done something wrong? I thought I had been working well, especially after all that I had been through, so I couldn't see that it was anything I had done to make her feel this way. She was looking at me so sadly. Did it mean bad news about my future with Hob Nob? I so hoped not, because this was the first time I had ever had a taste of what it was like to be properly cared for.

Jodie then did the most bizarre thing: she took off her hat, her coat and a jumper. Now, it wasn't summer so she couldn't have been warm! She walked on about four metres and stopped still. With her not moving a muscle I thought I would investigate her clothes – watching her all the time of course. There were no sinister smells, just smells of other animals, although none that I recognised from here or from my past – or is it that she IS an animal? After a while she quietly went off to get me some hay and left the barn, still looking a bit blue. I couldn't stop thinking about why she looked so depressed. Then I thought, ah, maybe the elephant noise brought her bad news! Little did I appreciate that it was indeed potentially bad news. From that day on it seemed that Hob Nob's body language changed towards me as well. Did she not want me any more or did she need the space for her other horses? What was to become of me? I was just beginning almost to trust Hob Nob! I started to think the worst; that I would be sent back to one of my previous homes. Would I ever see Jodie again? Although I was still fed and watered I was beginning to feel rejected once more, and decided that I would never trust anyone again because I just end up hurt.

A few days later I heard the old familiar sound of Jodie's car. Maybe she would help me through this bad stage. She came into the corridor and then the arena, looked at me in silence for about ten minutes, just as I did her, but instead of working with me she walked straight back out again. I so wanted her to work with me and to share even just a few moments of understanding. I stretched my head over the barn wall to watch what she was doing.

Instead of getting back in her car she went to the log house, knocked on the door and went in. She must have been there for at least half an hour, then she came back to see me. Her body language looked a bit better – perhaps she was even a bit happier. The change in her made me change – it was as if my gut instinct was that something was going to be happening; I just didn't know what. I so hoped that the contact made between Jodie and me wouldn't be jeopardised in any way.

Well, I never saw Jodie here again! For the next week or so I kept thinking about the happy times jumping the jump and the kind of two-way communication we had together, 50-50 almost. It had been so reassuring.

Hob Nob's routine stayed the same for another few days, although I felt as if I was being shoved from stable to barn for convenience! Perhaps it was so that the other horses that took humans on their backs could go round and round in circles, but some of them did get to go over my jumps – I felt a bit mythed about this! I could see and hear the lorry and trailer going out every so often. Sometimes horses would be taken away and not come back – I often wondered where they went to and would I end up going as well? Sometimes new horses would arrive but I never really got the chance to know them; anyway, I was still a bit scared of other horses, a result, I suppose, of the singleton life I had had to endure in my past.

Chapter 7

Oh no! I'm on the road again

'Oh no, it's a trailer for me'

AS HAD HAPPENED before, I could hear the trailer being moved to the entrance of the barn, but when my door opened I wandered out, thinking I was going into the arena as usual. But, oh no, the arena gate was tight shut and the corridor was blocked at the bottom end. I had no option but to turn right – and there was the trailer just in front of me!

Someone was behind me, so I couldn't go back because I might hurt them. In my panic I found myself in the trailer, and the ramp door banged shut. I didn't know what to think. Where was I going? What was I going to do? I thought I could trust Hob Nob! But thankfully she was there, at the front – phew – but oh no, she's trying to put a halter on me! I panicked a bit, but with everything happening so quickly and my thoughts racing at 100 miles an hour it was on before I knew it. The side door was shut and the trailer started moving. Would I ever be back in my luxurious stable? Would I ever get my regular feed and fresh water? Would I ever get a Hobnob again? All these thoughts were too much for me, and my past experiences came flooding back.

Before I knew it, however, the trailer had stopped. I whinnied for someone, I didn't know who; I just wanted to see someone I knew, I wanted to feel safe. After what seemed like a decade the little side door opened. Oh, what a relief! It was Hob Nob. But I heard another voice I recognised, yes, yes, yes, it's Jodie! The side ramp door opened and out I came with my head held high and with Hob Nob somehow attached. In my excitement I wasn't thinking how close she was. I just wanted to see where I was and to check that everything seemed safe.

I wondered if this was the place that the other horses had been taken to? But no, I didn't recognise any horsey sounds! There was one noise I kind of recognised, though – it was a very low barking sound, one that I could hear from Hob Nob's place! Phew, at least I'm not far away from that cosy stable, I thought. Maybe I'll be going back there soon?

I hadn't been out of Hob Nob's barn for a few days, so seeing daylight was a bit of a shock to the system. It was kind of exciting but I couldn't help wondering what was going to happen to me now.

I turned a few circles, trying to catch the skyline to see if I recognised it, but there were too many trees in the way to see; plus I was being pulled to go in another direction. I so wished for the feeling of safety that I had begun to feel with Hob Nob!

Before I knew it, I was going through a bright white gate and into another barn. It was smaller than Hob Nob's, but there was a massive bale of hay in it and a smaller gate to the left and sweet-smelling hay nets dangling from the middle. The ground seemed to be covered in shavings, which tickled my heels a bit. To the right there was a big chest with what looked like a whole heap of horse rugs on top and there were little coloured things along the side of the long white wall. There was a huge red tub filled to the brim with fresh water as you walked towards another gate at the far end of the barn. Then, all of a sudden, I was in a wee mini yard with total daylight.

The double barn doors were closed, which meant I couldn't go back to looking for the horizon, but little did I realise that I would get a chance to see it all again in a few days' time.

There were quite a few doors and windows, all in a cheery red and white. I wanted to investigate all the doors that were open but I wasn't too sure of them so, to start with, I stood outside for a few moments to smell the air coming from them.

Jodie encouraged me to explore, still with Hob Nob somehow attached to me. There was so much to see and to take in that I found myself wanting to go round it all again and again till I had picked up the scent from every corner of each outbuilding. It was a bit like one little circuit where you started off at one end and ended up back where you had begun.

There were other horsey smells, none of which filled me with anxiety. As I know only too well, when a horse has been in distress they can sometimes have the 'runs', which leaves a very particular smell as a warning sign. I didn't sense this at all; in fact, quite the reverse. It seemed like a happy, relaxed yard with quite a few horses somewhere about.

After about 15 minutes Hob Nob left, which meant there was now only Jodie, me, the dog with the deep bark and another couple of dogs. I couldn't resist the sweet-smelling hay or indeed the little hay net of haylage. When I took a mouthful it made the hay net swing, knocking against some very soothing chimes. How odd, but one of the four chimes had a certain pitch that made my back feel all goose bumpy. I had to give my whole body a shake because I didn't understand that feeling – I think it was a positive feeling, though.

I was aware by now that the barn really wasn't that big, so I was adamant that if anyone came within a four-metre radius of me I would bolt to the other side. I was not going to be captured by anyone.

Chapter 8

Phew, it's Hat lady's yard

'Mm, what's in here?'

I COULDN'T HELP but wonder why I had to be taken to yet another yard, but to be honest I couldn't have asked for anyone better to be at that yard than Jodie. Although I was aware that I didn't understand her one little bit I knew, deep down, that there was something very different about her and above all she didn't shout or scream; in fact I rarely heard her talk.

Hob Nob's yard was big enough to get away from anyone but this one wasn't. So, if someone was moving around, the only thing I could do was stay as far away from them as possible, even if it meant gluing myself to the opposite wall! Given the chance, I would get out of that area somehow.

Hob Nob's barn wall was about six or seven feet high on one side and to the roof on the other, but here the walls were 20 foot-plus. I knew I would never be able to jump them. I had noted, however, that I could – if push came to shove – jump the ten-foot by five-foot barn gate into the yard where the bright-coloured stable doors were.

After about an hour of being here I had settled in the barn with my hay (and partly attached chimes), with the gate to the yard open. I heard the closing of a wooden door then footsteps, the ringing of different chimes and what sounded like a freezer lid being opened! I so wanted to see what was going on but didn't dare; plus the hay was too sweet to miss and the chimes incredibly soothing. Still, the wind told me something tasty was coming in my direction. I turned round with the yard in view.

Everything smelt totally different to the smells at Hob Nob's. But it was a good smell. I heard the tap of a bucket – I knew that one from my past, so it had to be food – and my big ears pricked up as Jodie approached and then walked past the barn gate with the bucket! Where was she taking it to? Don't tell me I'm going to have to start mentally working already? Goodness gracious me, I have only just arrived! But no, she walked past again and placed the bucket in the middle of the yard where I could see it and walked away. Well, I wasn't going to miss out on a bucket of feed, that's for sure, so I gingerly walked up the gentle, three-metre long ramp and had a keek round the corner. No sign of anyone, not even the dogs, so I felt I could safely tuck in without the threat of being cornered or grabbed. It was delicious, whatever it was. With no one in sight and nothing to be too fazed about, I went back into the barn to finish the hay with the odd gulp of lovely fresh water to wash it all down with.

An hour or so later the wooden door opened again and I could hear footsteps. Two lights suddenly went on, one in the yard and two in the barn. Oh well, that's good because I didn't like the idea of being in the barn in the dark after the winter sun went down. For some reason Jodie closed the yard gate, which perplexed me a bit – but as soon as the three dogs came running out I guessed it was so they wouldn't run around my legs. I didn't see the dogs or Jodie again for a good half-hour but I did hear the big deep bark of one of them; which one it was I wasn't sure.

A wee while later my hay net was finished. Jodie walked past the yard gate again but disappeared, all of a sudden to reappear at the far end of the barn, near where the big hay bale was. This would have been about 12 metres away from me so I felt a little safe, but not for long because she was heading back into the barn in an attempt to tie the hay net up. She was considerate, though – she stopped before entering and watched me for a few moments, I guess to try and work out how she was going to tie it up without frightening me! I had a major problem with all this, because if I stood where I was it would mean that she would have to walk past me at a distance of no more than four metres and that would be just too close. She took one pace at a time, stopping for a few moments in between, making sure I wasn't going to panic.

With the whites of my eyes showing out of fear, I moved slowly towards the furthest part of the barn to allow her to tie the hay net up, all the time aware of every movement she made. She continued to move gingerly, then she slowly lifted a hand to put the hay net string through the loop. Well, that was enough for me! I was sure I was going to get wholloped. I was off, careering straight past her but at the furthest possible distance away.

I was blocked by the gate into the yard! It had to go, I had to get out – BANG, CRACK and CLATTER, the gate was down, but not down far enough for me to get out. I looked round to see where she was, and she had moved back to the big wooden doors and was crouching down. I remembered what the crouching down meant in Hob Nob's barn, so didn't feel quite so threatened, but I still had to get out! So I reversed, thought about it, and to finish the gate off, so that I could get out, I trampled on top of it! Unscathed, unhurt, I couldn't believe it. I was okay, but more to the point, I didn't get chased, cornered, roped up, shouted at or indeed hurt. Jodie spoke softly for the first time: 'That was a silly thing to do, you know, I have never hurt you and I never will.' Mmm, I thought.

All I know is that I did a dashed good job of that gate never being whole or indeed hung again! She left me in the yard to assess everything while she stood scratching her head and wondering, I guess, how she was going to repair the damage I had done. Now, Jodie may have been a quiet, small human, maybe just up to my shoulders in height, but after what I saw of her taking down the broken gate I reckon she must be very strong. Not only did she take it off its huge hinges but she broke it up into three bits AND carried them away! She's not a human to take on lightly, I think.

Then I heard clanking and clanging sounds that I didn't like at all, but it was Jodie carrying an old rusty gate, which she tied on to the existing gate hinges and covered with a big blue blanket (maybe so that I couldn't see the holes in it!). Then she ushered me gently back into the barn and closed it, although I couldn't understand why she should want to do that. Did she want me to break this new gate as well?

For the next few hours I listened to some soothing dolphin music and checked out all the new noises, like cars driving past and the wooden door opening and closing – which generally resulted in Jodie popping her head through the gate, I guess to make sure I was okay.

Although I had only arrived at this yard a few hours before I felt extremely relaxed, even with all the strange things around me. There was even a Santa sleigh, led by Rudolph the red-nosed reindeer, staring at me!

It wasn't long till something big stopped outside, making the ground underneath me vibrate. Maybe it was a big lorry or a bus – I couldn't see it because the large double barn doors were closed (probably to stop me from bolting out on to the road or from breaking yet another gate!). Jodie started to speak softly to someone and I wondered who it could be. Was it Hob Nob with a big lorry? No, it was a child. Yippee! But it was a child I didn't recognise and it sounded like a little boy. I like children; they have never done me any wrong. I couldn't wait to see this little person, but that wasn't to be for another hour or so.

The dogs were barking intermittently. After a while I realised that I could see through a part of the Big Barn doors, courtesy of a wooden knot that must have fallen out. Eventually I connected the barking with people walking past on the road, some of whom had dogs as well – and some were riding on horseback! Mmm, I thought, I wonder if that will ever be asked of me? I don't think I will ever have the confidence to have a human on my back, not after all that they have done to me.

The wooden door opened and shut again. This time it was Jodie and the little person. The dogs were so excited about both of them coming out, and I should have been excited as well. My ears pricked up to see if I could catch the tone of their voices. They seemed gentle, so perhaps I could stay calm? As before, I pretended I was totally concentrating on the few strands of hay I had left, but really I was watching them all the time – and I could see them both peering through the old rusty gate! It wasn't often that Jodie said much when she was around me, so for some reason I picked up on the few words that she did say and one of those sentences she kept repeating was: 'You must stay calm,' she said to the little boy. 'She's very scared.'

Jodie asked him not to go into any stable that I might be in, because nobody knew how I might react (little does anyone realise that I just need to be loved and cared for, but have been just too scared to accept these feelings). They both stayed outside for about an hour – I could see them going back and forward with buckets and more hay nets. Was it feeding time at the zoo? How many animals are there here, I wondered.

Chapter 9

My new stable mate – Billy Bob

'My new found painted friend'

LATER ON THAT evening Jodie appeared without the little person at foot, to check on me and must have decided that I needed to be moved, although the purpose was unclear. Maybe, like at Hob Nob's place, other animals needed to come in. I so wanted to have another look around the place but my lack of courage wouldn't let me. I was gently ushered into the yard and given the freedom of it – and of one of the stables with a red and white door. It had a view of the yard, the barn and all the other stables and of a big white stone box with windows in it … ah, so that's where the wooden door sound comes from! It must be Jodie's stable.

My stable was about five metres by five metres, quite a good size. The walls were white and a long refectory table ran along one side. There was what looked like a hay shed at the other – all within easy reach as well. Don't think I'll ever starve here!

As I turned round, I noticed a pony behind the table. It didn't move or speak to me, which was strange, but being wary of all horses, I stayed well away till I was pretty sure it wasn't going to turn round to kick me or indeed pull toady faces. Eventually, though, thoughts of all that hay got the better of me so I very quietly went to assess the situation. The pony still didn't move! I came closer and I realised it was a life-sized painting of a pony with the name Billy Bob written beside it! Aw, that's nice, I thought, I've got a non-threatening pony to keep me company! He was a dark bay with a little star on his forehead; a bit grey round the muzzle and cheeks, though. Beneath his very tidy forelock was a pair of exceedingly kind-looking eyes. I think I would like him as a friend, I thought. I wonder if I will ever meet him – or is his painting just a memorial to him?

Although I was busy investigating this new stable my ears were on red alert all the time, to the point where if I heard Jodie I would go and hide in a corner, hoping she wouldn't see me. At one point she popped her head round the door, but that was too much and I had to get out, so I flew past her, leaving my hay and my new-found painted friend, Billy Bob, behind. I waited till Jodie was well out of my way then meandered gently back into this new stable, reassessed it just in case she had put anything new into it and returned to eating my hay, accompanied by Billy Bob on the wall. I also tested out the stable hay sidewall, to see if I could reach the bales in the event that my hay net should not be kept filled. I could, yippee!

I was so busy eating and looking at Billy Bob that I 'didn't hear some other animals coming in until I heard a whinny. My ears pricked up and I grew my usual two feet taller. Although unsure, I strode out, looking very smart and pretended to be brave (thank goodness for the gate between us) as if to say to whoever you are – don't dare think of coming into my new stable! Had the gate been open, though, I would have run off to a corner and tried my best to become invisible.

Chapter 10

My new neighbours

'Ralphi and me'

I SPOTTED A DARK bay horse about the same size as me (16'2), a little grey Arab x Welsh, then in waltzed another two – a little chestnut Shetland and a bay (smells like female) Welsh cob. She pulled the most petrifying faces at me, though – I think I should stay well away from her. I sensed there was another one somewhere but I couldn't see him or her from where I was.

The only one that showed an interest in me was the little grey! I wonder why he was being so nice. I'm not used to anything being friendly to me, apart from Hob Nob, and of course Jodie. Whichever way, I was glad to have a gate and a fence between us because it gave me an extra sense of security.

The other horses seemed unfazed by my presence and started to make themselves at home by eating their hay and feed. So I followed suit, although on my way back inside I found a massive bucket of fresh water that I couldn't resist taking some large gulps from – just in case the water here became 'scarce' like it did in the old days across the sea.

So, my first evening in yet another yard! It's okay, but what will tomorrow bring? Lights went out at about nine o'clock in Hob Nob's stable. I wonder when they will go out here? I truly don't like the dark and kind of hope that the lights will stay on all the time.

The evening was still and all that could be heard was munch, munch, munch, with the odd chime being set off by either the dark bay or the little grey. The warm smell of the wood shavings in my stable was wonderful and made me really want to lie down. Should I risk it? Will someone come and grab me, rope me or hurt me?

I couldn't bear the thought of all that happening again so I decided to sleep standing up, with one ear wide awake. A good job too, because THUD! I jumped to attention to discover a ginger thing with a waving tail sitting on the refectory table staring at me. I snorted and darted as fast as I could into the yard, waking everyone up in the process. What a commotion! All the horses were staring at me, as if to say 'and what was that all about, you silly sausage?' I tried to explain by turning my head towards my stable a few times, and eventually they did the same. Then a few seconds later the little ginger monster meandered out. The wise old mare explained it to me: 'That's just Ginger Beer,' she said in her own sweet way. 'He'll be sitting on your back soon!' 'I don't think so,' I said. 'Just you wait and see! Mmm I thought, and with that my new-found equine acquaintances about-turned and ignored me.

It wasn't long after this that Jodie appeared out of her white box. Was she going to turn the lights out? Am I going to get some more tea? Or hay? Well, I could hear the sound of rattling buckets. Mmm, food! The other horses whinnied so there must be something nice afoot. While Jodie was doing what she was doing I raked the ground below the hay net for any strands that had fallen but, as always with one ear alert to noises from outside. Jodie came towards my stable with an armful of lovely smelling feed buckets. Mmm, is one of these for me? But she by-passed me altogether! How dare she? Oh, how I could do with a wee morsel! Just then I heard her returning. She stopped a bit away from my stable door with bucket in hand – did I dare go out? I so wanted to, but the light wasn't that bright and because of the shadows I couldn't see her very well. I couldn't see what she might have behind her back, or in her other hand, so reluctantly I stayed back – even although the smell was awesome!

Chapter 11
Hat lady doesn't give up easily!

'Me being stubborn'

WELL, IF I THOUGHT I'd have to starve for the night I obviously wasn't going to be allowed to. No sooner had Jodie's footsteps faded into the distance than she was back again – but bucketless! She stood outside my door, but to the side, for what seemed like a decade. What was she planning? The entrance to my stable was a good size but the refectory table was immediately to the right and to the left there was a narrow, slatted extra gate, angled inwards, so, whichever way she came in, I could batter her! Yep, that's what I'd do – although deep down I have never wanted to hurt anyone, least of all her.

I didn't know what to make of her as she moved into the doorway, her hands and head totally motionless. She took half a step forward; I immediately went to the back but to the opposite corner of my stable. A few moments later she took another half step forward; I turned round, ready to bolt if necessary. Then she took another quarter step, still with the rest of her body motionless, but by this time she was far enough in that I wouldn't be able to reach her even if I did want to batter her! Oh, she's a clever cookie, this one!

I made a dash for the door and before I knew it I was out having my face washed by the drizzling rain! I was standing where I thought I'd be safe, beside the other horses but with the gate between us, When Jodie came out of my stable and shut the door behind her. Oh No! That means I can't get in to polish off the licks of my hay! She's miserable! Then she slowly walked up the far wall towards the chiming/feed room door and brought out a bucket, yes, the one with the awesome-smelling food in it! I would have loved to have the confidence to take it straight from her hand but no, I couldn't. Realising I wasn't going to take it, she backed away, hoping, I suppose, that I would go forward to eat it, but no, I just couldn't bring myself to move.

In the past I have had feed buckets put down for me but that was just so people could grab me to do whatever they wanted to me. I wasn't ever going there again. But I had learned that if I pretended to fall asleep, people would get fed up with waiting and would just place the bucket on the ground somewhere and walk away. Which left me free – once I knew they were well out of reach or, depending on the person, completely out of sight – to go over and eat my fill.

No one had ever just waited until I took my feed, so I didn't think Jodie would be any different. But, believe it or not, she stood outside in the yard for five hours until I gingerly went up to the bucket. If she flinched a muscle, or came anywhere within 11 metres of me I would back off completely and go back to my pretend sleep until she had been motionless for a lengthy period of time.

To be totally but silently honest, it was lovely having someone standing with me while I was eating my tea. No one has ever spent that amount of time with me in one go, being perfectly silent; in fact never has anyone dedicated a whole five hours to me in one day, even with breaks in between. Could this be the start of something positive in my life, or will she give up and eventually consider me no use or a lost cause, like all the other people have? Or can she see the kindness in my big dark eyes? *How I so hope that I can find myself a home where I will be adored for who I am and not mocked or abused because of how I look or how I react.*

After finishing my tea – keeping one eye glued to Jodie all the while for signs of potential movement – I backed up so as not to get any closer to her, and had a lovely refreshing drink from a huge bucket, the like of which I have never seen before. Then I went back slowly to my stable for some more sweet-smelling hay. I couldn't believe that it was almost dawn! I could see from my stable that the other horses were staring at me with faces that seemed green with envy. Did I look odd or something? Had I changed colour since they saw me last? Or was it just because it had taken me so long to have the courage to eat my tea? They had all finished their hay by now and could see my hay net still standing full!

Jodie's footsteps disappeared and didn't reappear for a few hours. During that time I sensed it was safe, apart from when Ginger Beer (the ginger cat) jumped up in an attempt to introduce himself. He gave me a fright each time. I kept thinking to myself, 'Maybe one day I'll not be so frightened of such a little furry creature that has springs for legs!' Anyway, I managed somehow to get forty winks, undisturbed by humans. In between dozing I would go out and have a wander round the yard to assess what the other horses were doing. Two of them seemed fairly friendly but the bay mare still pulled toady faces at me.

Chapter 12
My first morning with Hat lady

'My stable door'

AS DAWN TURNED into daylight Jodie reappeared, walked round everyone to say her good mornings then let the dogs out and disappeared again with a plastic bag in hand (smelt good from a distance). A few moments later I heard the sound of bleating sheep! Perhaps the food she was carrying was for them? Wish she had given me some first.

Returning with a squished-up bag (foodless), she gathered six feed buckets together and took them to what I think was the feed room. En route the wind chimes must have been given a knock, and all the other horses responded by neighing. Ha ha! Breakfast time – yippee!

A few moments later the other horses changed their tone as they heard her footsteps heading back out of the feed room. Now then, I thought, I should be first because I am the one closest to the feed room. But no, she had the audacity to walk straight past me! Not that I would have taken it straight away anyway, but that's not the point. It was the toady-faced mare that was the lucky one. Then the little cheeky-faced Shetland pony – the thing that seemed half the size of a grasshopper! She went back for more buckets and returned, and it still wasn't me that got the next load of feed. It was the big dark bay, the little grey and then the one in the distance that I hadn't seen yet but who I had heard whinnying earlier.

Not before time, she went back for another bucket – a big bright floppy yellow one with two handles. The smell was just mouth-watering! But I had the same problem as before – I was too scared to go out of my stable to get it. Ah, that's why she fed the others first: she knew I would take for ever.

Oh, dear. I so wanted that food, but I just could not go out while Jodie was there, even with her being ten metres away. I know she had put the dogs in, so they wouldn't upset me, and I know she was standing perfectly still and did stand perfectly still for an hour, but I just couldn't risk it. Oh how I yearned for just a wee taste! A bit like the Bisto Kid on the television, my nose was like a magnet to the steamy sugar beet! I couldn't resist it any longer. One slow step at a time, I ventured out and stopped three paces from my bucket. Jodie moved back three paces with the rest of her body still. Could I go forward, should I go forward, would she suddenly grab me? I took another pace forward; she took a pace back. Mmm, now that's kind! I wonder if I were to take another pace forward whether she would take another one back? YES, I have cracked it! She's still a safe ten metres away.

I put my head down part way, not sure whether I should submerge my head in the bucket as I wouldn't be able to see her then. I lowered it a bit more – she still didn't move. I gave out a little squeak, just as you would if you were about to take that first step towards letting go before your first bungee jump or your first parachute jump from an aeroplane. I had to have a poo, I was so scared. I quickly put my head down, grabbed a mouthful, thinking: is she still in the same place, has she got a rope in her hand? Then I darted back up. PHEW, she hasn't moved a muscle, maybe I could try that again! I lowered my head a bit again, checked for movement, and zapped back down for another mouthful, letting out a second squeal at the same time. My squeal of fear is how any animal will react when they are extremely scared. It's not just horses that do it. It means: please, please don't hurt me! It's the sound a human would make if they felt threatened by some sort of big monster and had nowhere to run to. Perhaps you can relate to this this petrifying feeling.

It took me a further hour to finish my breakfast and I can tell you, every squeal was worth it, because breakfast was just delicious. Dare I say it was even better than Hob Nob's breakfast? Sorry, Hob Nob! Jodie was still motionless so I reversed back two paces for a long drink of cool water out of that awesome bucket that never seemed to run dry. It was perfect – fresh water, as refreshing as an ice tea or a pint of lager shandy to a thirsty human on a scorching sunny day, and there whenever I wanted it. What a lucky mare I am! It wasn't the tin-tasting, black shale water that had been all there was to drink when I was younger. In fact it was so good that whenever I took a mouthful I would keep it in my mouth for at least five minutes, savouring every droplet, before swallowing it – not an easy task! But when you have been starved of something there's no way you won't take as much of it as possible when that something is right in front of you – no matter how many gallons, litres, tonnes or kilos there is of it!

Jodie had gone into the barn by this time, although I am not sure why. I knew I had some fallen hay left so I meandered back inside to finish it – with, as always, one ear on red alert, just in case. And Billy Bob was there to keep me company. It was so nice to be able to go into a fresh-smelling stable and back out to the yard again, where the sun's rays could warm my back, instead of being in a dark barn or a dark tin shack without any window at all. I think I could like this place!

When I went out for a sup of water a little later I noticed that the other horses were no longer around. Where had they gone? I hadn't heard them leaving. I guess I was enjoying my freedom to daydream and think about positive thoughts in a positive light – what a pleasant change! A wee while later, the yard's barn gate opened. I assessed the situation, noting that Jodie wasn't around, and went in to discover two hay nets filled to the rim hanging from the centre. It seemed that not only did I have the bright sunny yard and a stable to walk into, I had the barn as well. How amazing, all this unthreatening space, with the soothing sounds of wind chimes and chirping birds. In fact it was so relaxing that I even found myself resting one hind leg.

A short while after this I heard Jodie's car going off and I didn't see her again for about four hours, but that was okay because I had the dogs around me. Their barks, far from frightening me these days, made me feel safe. Every so often, their tone would change, and I eventually connected this type of bark to people walking by.

Knowing that no humans were around, I even found myself lying down to have an undisturbed afternoon nap. It was just terrific, not having any mental or human pressure on me, although I was beginning to like the idea of my one-to-one attention. There was even a hint of warmth in my heart. I knew, deep down, that I still had a huge mountain – 'Mount Confidence' – to climb, but for the moment, I had experienced, for the first time ever, a few moments of absolute bliss with no weight on my shoulders. The only problem with this feeling was the aftermath – It felt like the weight of a ten tonne elephant, or as if I had run ten 100km marathons: I was totally exhausted.

Was it because, for the first time in a very long time, I had been able to relax? I don't think I had realised how exhausted I was or how much I had been running on automatic pilot. Whatever the reason, I so hoped I could experience more of these totally magical moments – hooves crossed!

I heard what I thought was Jodie's car return, a rustle of bags and the car doors shutting. I remembered there was a wee hole in the tall barn double doors, so I lowered my head just to double-check, and yes, it was Jodie. I didn't see her for a wee while but just as dusk fell she came out, checked me through the gate and proceeded to fill and tie up the hay nets in all the stables except for the ones in the barn where I was. Mmm, why aren't I getting any? Moments later, I was – very gently this time – ushered back into the yard and then to the stable I had been in the night before, and sure enough, there was a large hay net waiting for me.

The dogs were out this time but I wasn't too fazed by them. When the other horses came in, though, and I ventured to the gate to try and smell where they had been, I was charged at from the other side of the gate by the little obnoxious grey Arab x Welsh gelding. I'll not do that again in a rush, I thought! But maybe I will be allowed out tomorrow to the place where they were today? That would be something to look forward to – a place where

I could maybe roll in the mud! There might even be a tree I could scratch myself against – what a lovely thought.

It wasn't long before the dogs were put in and I gathered tea was being served. The smell was wonderful. Would I be last in the queue again? Would I be able to pluck up the courage to take it a bit sooner than last night, or would the fear of being caught override my hunger pangs again?

Indeed it did. I couldn't cope with eating while Jodie was anywhere near me, so I stayed in my stable. We went through exactly the same procedure as the night before. Jodie gently encouraged me out, shut my stable door so I wouldn't go back in, and stood perfectly still for after five hours while I intermittently pretended to doze in a corner. Eventually, again, I plucked up the courage to go forward, with the same anxiety and squeals as the night before. What I hadn't noticed last night was that the others get an extra titbit, almost like a pudding, before most of the lights are put out, and I didn't get one! At least I thought I hadn't got one, until I had a wander in the yard later and sniffed my feed bucket and sure enough, there was a Rich Tea biscuit – a midnight snack – lovely.

RESCUE PART 2

Make this my home,
A field to roam,
Sun on my back,
Friends of my own.

I'm frightened today!
Memories burn,
No-one must touch me!
Nightmares return.

I must BELIEVE the wonder of this,
The company I keep,
I quietly weep,
My special friend,
Small and sweet,
She lights my life,
Has banished strife.

I look for her each dawning day,
I KNOW she feels my spirit pray,
She calms and fills my aching heart,
With Hope.

Written by L.F. Scottish Borders

Chapter 13

My first day out!

'Running free'

THE NEXT DAY it was a gorgeous bright sunny morning. Jodie went away with the dogs and the nice-smelling bag for, I assumed, the bleating sheep, returned and fed the other horses, but instead of waiting for me this time she placed my bucket on the concrete and disappeared. Now, why couldn't she do that all the time? It wouldn't take me five hours to eat it then!

Once breakfast was finished and the dogs put back in, Jodie obviously had a different plan for today. I could hear the others being rugged up, and the sound of their hooves in mud. I heard gates and doors being shut and the yard gate being opened. Should I venture out to look? Well, curiosity got the better of me. Out I went through the barn and its large wooden doors, to find Jodie standing on the inside of the roadside gate with the horizon behind her, the same horizon I had so wished to see when I first arrived. She had her back to me, which seemed odd, but it was okay; I didn't feel threatened – at least until I turned right. Suddenly I couldn't see Jodie because of the bend in my body and I was off, hell for leather, my head held higher than ever before, my tail sticking almost straight up and my legs stretching out to the most beautiful trot I had ever seen myself do and my neck swinging from side to side, as I kept an eye on all that I passed. I was as free as a bird! I could almost feel myself flying – it was awesome. I felt like a foal running for the very first time or a cloud gliding through the sky – FREEDOM with a boundary fence!

My elation didn't last long. Suddenly the little half-pint Shetland snuck under the fence that was separating me from the others – I had had the audacity to look at his toady-faced mare – and chased me all the way round the field at least eight times, me ducking my head under tree branches and running through a wood as fast as I could go. My poor legs hadn't been running like this for a long time – they were beginning to ache. When would he stop chasing me or let me stop? With the benefit of hindsight, I can see that having this little thing running in an attempt to keep up his chase was quite funny; his little legs must only have been about a foot and a half from the ground. Thelwell rings a bell! Eventually I could feel him tiring, because I wasn't running as fast, and at long last he did give up chase. But then the other pony, the little dark bay I hadn't seen before but knew was there, started off from where the other little horror left off! Eventually I got the message – I was to stay well clear of and not even be allowed to look at the toady-faced mare.

SIMPLE PLEASURES

Prancing and dancing
I feel so free,
A lovely field,
Is it for me?
Oh, I see the others - - -
Hope they won't chase!
The grass is green,
I want to graze!'
It seems to be fine
I'm going to pretend that
THIS FIELD IS MINE!

Written by L.F. Scottish Borders

Chapter 14
I've been adopted!

'Charlie Barnie'   Elaine Stewart

JUST AS THE LITTLE dark bay allowed me to stop, the grey Arab x Welsh pony came skidding up to about ten metres away, bowed his head, and submissively walked up to my side. I didn't move; he wasn't a threat, in fact I had a distant memory of each of my five differently coloured foals running up to me in the same way as this.

I froze, and found myself remembering those vague warming memories of giving birth and the special moments a mother has with her child from the moment they are born until, in my case, the dreadful day when they were snatched and taken away. Was this one of my foals? Why can't I remember the smell? Was it because I wasn't allowed to keep them for long, or was it because the negative things that have happened to me since have made me forget about those unique moments?

I was in a dream, wishing that this was one of my foals. I didn't notice at first that he was looking for some milk; anyway, I was dry, so I gave my head a shake. What am I doing, letting this total stranger try to take a suckle? My maternal instinct truly tickled the surface; I so wanted to mother him, but more to the point I wanted my own foals back. I so wanted to see them – I had often sensed that one wasn't well and that there was a chance the others might be dead. I so wished to see that they were all okay. If only there was a way!

In time both our necks were arched and our noses touching, as if we were so pleased to see each other after all these years. It was one of the most heart-warming experiences I had had for a long time. After a few moments like this we walked off together as if he was my foal at foot – yet another truly awesome and unforgettable moment to add to the memories of my own five little ones that I will treasure for ever.

The field the grey Arab cross encouraged me to walk in, albeit gingerly, was quite big – perhaps about five acres. It had a five-foot hawthorn hedge all the way up the left-hand side, a wall going along half the width at the bottom, adjoining a wire fence with trees at the front and a stream running all the way along in between. The sound of fresh running water was wonderful but not nearly as awesome as it was for me to bathe my hot, badly cracked and misshapen hooves in – a wonderful cool babbling and rippling brook! Perhaps I did what you would do on a hot summer's day or if your muscles ached – you too might try some rippling water therapy, if not a mustard bath!

For the rest of that day my newly adopted dapple-grey son, whose name I learnt was Charlie Barnie, followed and stood by me wherever I went. If I raised my head and suddenly couldn't see him I'd whinny, and he'd come running back – I felt so humbled and comforted by this. Perhaps it was another hint that my battened-down, warm heart had been allowed to come to the surface. But would it stay there, or would it end up being shunted to the background again as it had been so often in the past? I tried so hard not to think about what might happen in the future but it was difficult, especially after having lived through such traumatic times. I guess this day taught me an important lesson, though:

Live each day as it comes, be grateful for the good things that happen within it and try to let the negative bits flow over you like water off a duck's back.

Chapter 15
Five new feathery friends

'The biting geese'   Elaine Stewart

TALKING OF DUCKS, also in the field were five feathery things that looked like overgrown ducks, all of whom attempted to charge me with their beaks snapping and aiming at my hairy fetlocks. This happened each time I went anywhere near them (I have since discovered that they were geese). It seems *the smaller the animal the more aggressive they are! Perhaps it's just because smaller things need to be heard and given the understanding that they are entitled to – a voice as well.* These ones didn't half make a noise, especially if there were people going up and down the road; in fact one of them had a real attitude problem – it must have been a boy goose! But there was a good point about this deafening noise – they became another one of my alarm systems, like the dogs.

However, back to my first day in the field, and the lessons I learnt. Well, I quickly gathered I was to keep my distance, by about forty feet, from the pretty, but toady-faced mare or I would be chased away by the little half-pint Shetland pony and the little dark bay. However, I thought it a bit unfair that Charlie Barnie was allowed to walk around her, albeit from a distance of about four metres. Maybe one day I might be accepted as part of a herd, just like a normal horse should be.

This day of being among my own kind made me realise I had led a very sad life – a bit like a Hermit's, in fact, as if I had been intentionally kept apart from other horses. Yet a horse is a natural herd animal, just as a dog is a natural pack animal. I had such a yearning to be part of a herd – would it ever happen, or was I to continue living on my own? I guess I had to learn how to become a horse again, before I could be part of any group. One thing for sure was that the other horses were giving me one quick lesson!

My spirits weren't strong enough to stand up to them, though, and I was scared of being chased and hurt yet again, even by my own kind.

While grazing, with my right eye on duty at all times, and with my adopted son at my side for most of the time, I watched to see how each of them interacted. Perhaps I could learn how to interact with others all in one day? It wasn't to be.

Chapter 16

Daylight turns to dusk

'Dusk'   Tom Brodie

I COULDN'T BELIEVE how quickly daylight started turning to dusk that day – *doesn't time pass when you are having fun*? Out came Jodie and the dogs. As soon as I saw them I headed off in the opposite direction, but Charlie Barnie didn't go with me; he went to Jodie. How dare he, I thought, what a turncoat! However, it was lovely to watch the dogs playing together and to see Jodie playing with them. Even she and Charlie Barnie had a wee frolic around; it looked like so much fun. Oh, how I wish I had the confidence to interact like that with anything – man or beast! Maybe one day.

As much as she was enjoying playing with all the dogs and other horses, Jodie eventually walked towards me. The other horses ignored her. Oh no, I thought. You are not coming to get me! But still she headed in my direction. She stopped about 30 metres away, which was enough to encourage me to walk on, but I wasn't quite sure what direction I was supposed to be going in. I think she sensed this, so she changed her direction a bit – so much so, that if she wanted me to turn right she would go to the left, or she'd go right if she wanted me to turn left. Again, I heard no shouting and saw no jumping up and down or the waving of any sticks. Eventually she managed to get me down across the stream, where I stopped for a drink, then through the barn gate and into the barn – in fact she did to me what the collie dog did with the sheep earlier on; she gently herded me. The sweet- smelling hay that hung by a rope from the middle of the barn made my mouth water, so on passing the big red bucket of water I'd drink as if there was no tomorrow. I don't think my memories of earlier days when I had no water at all or had to drink the horrible black-tasting shaley liquid will ever leave me.

Jodie shut the big double wooden barn doors from the outside, only to reappear at the other gate, where the obnoxious little dark bay had been the night before. She disappeared for another few moments then reappeared in the yard, where the dogs were waiting for her. She told them to stay – Mmm, what's she up to? – then slowly shut the yard's iron gate and came in using a smaller gate next to it. I turned round to eat my hay so that I could see her at all times. She stood there for ages, not staring at me but just leaning against a wall, resting a leg against it. Did she have a sore foot, or was she just relaxed? However it was, for as long as she was depending on just one leg she couldn't do much to hurt me, so I relaxed a bit and ate with a little more ease. Intermittently she would change legs, just like I do when I am resting; then she would slowly turn round and repeat this leg-resting habit. After half an hour or so she very slowly started to slide around the circumference of the barn with the leg rests in-between. There was no way I was going to let her do anything without me watching her, so I found myself slowly ambling round with her in full eye-shot and the thought that I could easily brake or bulldoze that old iron gate if she put too much pressure on me. Jodie was very considerate, though, and worked at a snail's pace with me –although at one point when I felt I had to walk up to the gate to get a drink, she had the audacity to walk into the centre and pull some of MY hay out of the net and pocket it! She stood there for ages, hands back down at her side and with an unthreatening posture, and eventually I plucked up the courage to walk along by the side of the wall, hoping that she would respond to my body language just as I had done with hers. But she didn't; she kept standing there, hogging my haynet! How dare she!

I stopped; she stayed still. I so wanted a mouthful of hay! But she didn't move for another 15 minutes. I was, as always, very hungry and beginning to fear that she had super-glued herself to the ground! I wasn't for budging but at long last she started to amble round to the other side of the hay net. I felt safe enough to walk a couple of paces towards where the rugs were; she remained still for another few moments and then moved quietly to the point where I had previously stood. *Is this reverse psychology, I wondered?*

I took a step sideways, with my back end angled towards her just in case; she didn't react or indeed budge, so I took another one and she still didn't budge. Not prepared to move any further, I stretched my neck out as far as I could, opened and tried to lengthen my blubbery lips as far as possible to tease out the only strand I could reach. Yes, I got it! She stayed where she was for about an hour, not moving, by which time I discovered that my feet had wandered closer to the hay net – leaving Jodie only five metres away. I was beginning to think that perhaps, just perhaps, she really wasn't out to hurt me. Could I afford to begin to believe this? I was unsure. After a further ten minutes with hands by her side she reversed back out of the barn and left me. I didn't flinch an inch – wow!

Every so often for the next few hours when I heard the wooden door bang I knew Jodie would appear shortly after – to check me, I guess. For the first time I decided to lie down, but didn't know where the safest place was. I assessed each area and eventually chose to lie next to the horses' rugs on the wooden chest. I wanted to see and smell them; I wanted to feel secure, and not be staring into a big open space. I tried to lie down as close as possible with just the rugs in view and my back facing the open space – oh for the feeling of security! I think at one point I heard the wooden doors close, but I was in too deep a sleep to be fully aware of it – at least, I didn't jump up to attention, so I must have felt safe.

Later on, just as on the previous night, I was ushered into my stable with the red and white door and the yard where another hay net was awaiting my consumption. The other horses were brought in and fed too – and I was last, as usual. I had hoped that Jodie would put my yellow-handled food bucket on the ground as she had done that morning, but no, an action replay of the night before took place and five hours later, at 3am, as the other horses slept, I finished my tea with Jodie still standing at a distance, but this time only about seven metres away. What a transformation! My nervous squeaks were still to be heard, so much so that the yellow dog, who I have since found out is called Star, responded by tilting her head to the side and letting out a wee cry herself. Perhaps another animal is beginning to understand my needs – wouldn't it be lovely if more than just two living creatures could start to understand me? Dream on, I told myself.

The dogs were taken out, then all the lights except the one in the yard were turned off for the night, or at least for another three hours, before the routine started again the next morning. I had noticed since my arrival that Jodie's stable light rarely went out for at least another hour after our one and it was turned on about 30 minutes before she came out in the mornings. She must be a worse sleeper than me! Through the night I would sometimes have a wee wander about the yard, making sure everything was safe, then I'd have a look to see what the other horses were up to. Nine times out of ten they were eating or sleeping; rarely did they come over to see me, although sometimes little Charlie Barnie would turn round to acknowledge me. But that's about all. At the top of the yard I could see that Jodie was still up because the light in what looked like a busy kitchen would still be on. I could see her fingers thumping away at a wee flat black thing with a screen attached. Why did a silly little black thing, that didn't look as if it even moved, require her attention so often? Was I experiencing a touch of jealousy?

The next morning I felt Jodie was in a bit of an anxious rush. She seemed flustered and eager for us all to finish our breakfast, putting my yellow bucket down in the yard for me to eat without a bystander. Yippee, I could eat it straight away! She even fed the sheep at a different time and the rugs were put on the others as soon as they had finished; then it was out to the field for all of us.

I was last as usual, but that was fine because I was able to bathe my scraggy hooves in the rippling stream while the others were heading up to the top of the field. Just as I was about to attempt to jump out of the stream Charlie Barnie came galloping down, as if to say, 'Come on, we are all up there, you come too.' So we went off together with a bit of

My thin aching body, scarred muzzle and my new friends

My name is changed to Lauder Lass thanks to Lauder folk

Jodie judging at Dogs Allowed Show Thirlestane Castle 2010.
Drawings created by members of the public

Lauder Lass's door plaque and some cards created by Border Beads and Joan

My adopted son Charlie Barnie and some of my visitors

A winter's morning

A new day dawns as I realise I can be brave to speak to my visitors after all

Thank you all

Thank you all for your continuing kindness, without it I would never have been able to cross my fear barriers so soon.

WHERE THERE WAS ONCE DESPAIR THERE IS NOW HOPE
I WISH I COULD TELL EVERYONE "NEVER EVER GIVE UP"

a buck and a rear. *It felt so good, running _with_ another horse. This wasn't running away from something, it was running _with_ someone and for fun*. Most importantly, I was free. From a distance I could see Jodie exercising the dogs, and then I heard her car engine start. I didn't see her again till much later.

Dusk was drawing in and still no sign of Jodie. I didn't like the dark and wanted to be back in my stable, or at least the barn where I felt safe. I was getting worried – was she okay? Why should she be late? She was the only one here that tended to us horses. Then I was wondering what would happen to me if something happened to her. I got myself into an awful panic until, from a distance, cheeky Charlie Barnie must have sensed this and decided to meander up to me and start to muzzle my shoulders for a one-to-one grooming session. I returned the favour. Bless him, it did take my mind off things, but the best thing was that he stayed by my side until Jodie returned, although this seemed very late and well after dark.

I hadn't known Jodie to be as late as this before. I didn't know any other human, apart from Hob Nob, but she hadn't been down to see me since I arrived here, so I felt as if she had almost washed her hands of me, which stirred, once again, that feeling of 'I'm a lost cause'.

Charlie Barnie was still near me when the 'Jodie's back' message reached us via the dogs barking; this was a happy bark, not the alarm call reserved for strangers. Sure enough, moments later the dogs were all running around the field. There was a downside to this; something horrible was with them, a round white thing that moved as they were moving; it made shadows. My hooves alert and ready to run, I remembered these white things from somewhere else I had been and the unhappy memories came flooding back. My neck grew and I raced to the opposite end of the field. Charlie Barnie didn't know what to make of my sudden need to run but came with me, snorting and waving his head from side to side as if a monster had come out of the hawthorn hedge. Shortly afterwards, he gave himself a big shake as if to say, 'And what was all that about?' The other horses completely ignored this white light, so I was a trifle confused, but I tried hard to calm down a bit.

Jodie had obviously realised how I had reacted to the white thing (it was a torch) and turned it off, using what little moonlight there was instead. She brought the dogs in to heel and herded me gently down through the stream. Remembering how I had enjoyed going through it the night before she took the pressure off me by stopping a good distance away, so that I could have a soak and a drink before going through the gate and into the barn for the hay that had already been hung. The only difference now was that Charlie Barnie chose to come down with me. I don't think he liked getting his clean, neat and tidy hooves wet, though, because I never heard the splish splash sound on his way in.

Charlie Barnie didn't come in the same way as me, I guess because we might have reacted badly had we been put together in a smaller area. Instead he was invited up the ramp where the little bay's stable was; but he chose to go back to his known herd. I was very touched that he stayed with me until he knew that I felt safe in the barn or yard. In fact, since then I have often thanked him for that – a momentous day for me, when another animal reassured me; I had never experienced this before. My heart felt full for the rest of the evening.

My hay net and water bucket had already been filled so I was quite happy munching away. Then I lay down next to the rugs again and found myself dozing, hearing the dogs occasionally barking in the background, the wooden door being opened and the ginger thing (Ginger Beer) darting through the barn every so often. I remember half-dozing and half-thinking that Jodie still seemed a bit blue. I didn't know what to do to cheer her up – if I was a normal horse I would have gone straight up to her, but I couldn't afford to do that yet and I think that was my last thought before I fell asleep. I didn't stir again for a couple of hours, until I heard Jodie filling up the hay nets for the other horses coming in. I must have been in a very deep sleep because I didn't even hear the wooden door open

or indeed the bolt being unlatched to the bottom stable which leads into the hay section of the barn I was in. I couldn't think when the last time was that I had slept so soundly. Was this my conscious beginning to relax as well?

After being gently roused I was ushered quietly into the yard – my thoughts: tea, yes, I'm getting another tea, I wonder if it will be as tasty as last night's? The evening meals always seem to taste different to breakfast. Oh, but will I have the confidence to eat it any quicker than last night? I so hoped that Jodie would get fed-up waiting and just place my bucket in the yard and go away again, just like everyone else in my past had done.

Eventually, through the walls, I heard the tea buckets being mixed up, saw each one going past my door except the one for me. This time my food didn't appear. I couldn't see Jodie. Should I venture out or should I not? I sensed she was outside my door somewhere, but I couldn't hear her. She stayed wherever she was for ages (about an hour) without giving me my tea. Once again, curiosity got the better of me so I stretched my head out of the door, using Billy Bob as my shadow. I could see her about seven metres away, but with no bucket in her hand or indeed on the ground. It seemed that as soon as I showed my head and made eye contact with her she reversed back towards the feed room. I ventured out, to check that she really *was* going to fetch my feed. Perhaps stretching my neck out had said to Jodie: 'Can I have my feed please?' Perhaps *I need to ask for things from now on, but in a way that is acceptable to her. Just like Charlie Barnie did, when he initially introduced himself to me, it was a way that I understood and one that he sensed I could cope with.*

I truly think Jodie is trying hard to communicate with me, but it's a question of whether, *after all I've been through, am I prepared to let myself be communicated with.* This lesson was a big one for me, but one that I am now actively and positively encouraged to build on.

Perhaps it's similar to the way a troubled human needs to learn a new way of communicating to get what they want from society; or it's like the way spouses, friends, and families have to change the way they communicate with a loved one suffering from a degenerative disease like Alzheimer's, or Vascular Dementia. As their illness progresses, sufferers find it more difficult to understand what is considered normal human language. Or think of the way a child eventually learns to ask a parent for something that they want but wouldn't, or indeed shouldn't, get if they asked in the wrong way.

After this instance I seemed to gain the courage to stay in the yard until Jodie slowly returned with my yellow feed bucket. She stopped nine metres away, laid the bucket down quietly and reversed a further seven metres. Once again I so wanted to go straight to my feed but was still unsure. I took a brave step forward but no, I couldn't go any further so I did my usual – I pretended to sleep, with one eye a quarter shut, making sure that Jodie wasn't going to move. Three hours later, I was still standing there, as was Jodie; my stable door was still open with hay in the net. I could have gone back in to eat my hay but chose to stay where I was. It was comforting having Jodie there but on the other hand I still didn't feel safe going straight to my bucket.

Realising that Jodie was as stubborn as me and that the wafting smell of the garlic in my tea was still destined for my stomach, I eventually plucked up the courage – an hour later –to sneak forward to my bucket. My legs stopped short, though, just in case I had to run so my neck had to stretch out for the first little mouthful. Well, this kind of worked because it meant that the bucket had to tilt a bit, which allowed me to keep an eye on Jodie instead of having my peripheral vision blocked by the sides of the bucket. A clever move on my part, I thought, but more importantly, it worked even with my little anxious squeals.

I managed to finish my tea with Jodie standing completely still, and returned unscathed to my hay. I heard the night-time titbits going round and really wanted my one; but *just as a child assumes there will be an after-school snack waiting for them when they get home*, I was quite sure that Jodie would leave my titbit in my bucket, so I left it until she was away for the night before I investigated. Shock! Horror! There was no titbit in my bucket! I was confused, never mind annoyed. ***Does Jodie not accept assumptions?*** Am I going to have to work for tomorrow night's treat? Time would tell. I do so want to overcome my fear of her, but I'm just too scared to let go. Maybe she wants me to try a little harder. I thought this over an evening's sleep, in between Ginger Beer giving me frights by jumping on my table.

In the morning, just after dawn, I was standing in the yard, day-dreaming. Jodie's stable was quiet and there was no movement to be seen but then I heard a very peculiar noise – like a machine-driven alarm; and then the lights went on. I saw Jodie mulling around with the little person wandering behind her. It must be breakfast time soon. Mmm, I like the breakfasts here. I had also realised, a few days before, that a big machine like a bus would pull up outside and shortly after that Jodie would appear to muck out and feed us. However, this day everything seemed to be in fast motion. She was out, we were fed, watered, briefly skipped out and put out to the field but before I could say boo to the goose, I saw the pick-up disappear in haste. Something must be wrong; maybe that's why she was a bit blue the other day. I was concerned, but found some security with young Barnie, who very kindly stayed with me for most of the day. The little half-pint had another go at chasing me but Charlie Barnie seemed to block him, a bit like the way the collie dog that lives here blocks the sheep.

Dusk was drawing in, but still no sign of Jodie, the little person or even the dogs, although I did hear them bark every so often. The dark came and still no sign. Where on earth is she? I don't like the dark. Half an hour or so later a different pick-up arrived. I half recognised it, but had forgotten who it belonged to until the voice appeared – it was Hob Nob! What's she doing here, I thought? She hadn't even come to visit me! The old let-down feelings bubbled to the surface again. I felt low. Was Jodie going to disappear on me? Just as I was thinking that Charlie Barnie gave me a nudge, as if to say, 'Snap out of it, girl, you'll be okay here, you'll see.' Mmm, I thought, I've been let down so many times before.

The dogs barked. Was she indeed someone I couldn't trust, or was it just that the dogs didn't know her? I didn't know what to think, but at least I had a field to run in so I knew there was no way that she could catch me. I'd stay close to Charlie Barnie – he'll make me feel safe, I thought.

I could hear the ramp stable door opening; out came the dogs, followed by Hob Nob who was dragging a big white bag behind her. Mmm, maybe she's come to give us some food. I wasn't sure of the noise of the bag though – the sound seemed to echo or bounce off the outside stable walls, or was it the wood in the middle of the field that was making the frightening noise? I didn't like it, it sounded like a sound from my past. I shuddered and shook and decided to stay safely away from the fearful noise so I trotted off to the opposite side of the wood. The sound didn't seem to perturb the other horses, in fact Charlie Barnie went running down towards it, coming to a skidding stop. Perhaps he wasn't sure of Hob Nob either? I was even more unsure because of his behaviour and wanted him to come back, for fear that something would happen to him as it did to my other foals. But I didn't have the confidence to protect him. The other horses followed suit and, as always, as soon as the toady-faced mare arrived on the scene, she chased the others away apart from the big bay and the Shetland – I think they are in cahoots with each other! Wouldn't it be nice if I could be accepted as part of the herd I thought again. Dream on, I told myself firmly.

It was during moments like these that I often wondered if it was just the equine world that ostracised some of its members or whether other animal breeds did the same. In my past, when I had been turned into a solitary horse by humans, I had often watched and wondered why individual breeds, like dogs and humans, ostracised each other. Was it because individuals looked different, just like I used to look different when I had my big ears or was skinny and scrawny, or was it because they acted differently just like I used to when I felt, and still do to a point, feel scared and anxious? Or was it more of a jealousy thing? Then again, perhaps life is just a permanent competition for some individuals – and not just horses. However it is, I know from my experiences to date that to be ostracised for whatever reason is 100 per cent depressing, demoralising and heart-wrenching and can make you feel even further out on a limb than you already are.

As Hob Nob made her way up the field she stopped every so often, bent over and pulled out an armful of hay and placed it on the ground, then walked on a bit further and did the same. She repeated this until there were seven piles, laid the bag down and walked towards me. I was off, not having anything to do with her at all, and bolted off to the furthest pile. By the time I had got to the last pile, the sheep were at it. Dischuffed at this, I hoofed the ground with my left foreleg and threatened to flatten one of them – they were off like a shot!

Hob Nob stopped and watched for a few moments then returned to her pick-up – without the bag. The night grew darker but still there was no sign of Jodie or indeed of the dogs running free in the field. Was she all right? It's unlike her to go away. I do hope she will come back, I thought.

A while later obviously something was up because the toady-faced mare started to pace the ground. I had never seen her do that before. In fact the only time I can remember pacing the ground worryingly were the days after my foals had been taken away. Maybe she is a wise mare, maybe I should respect her after all, perhaps she has the kind of relationship with Jodie that all animals wish for. In fact, her behaviour made me think I should stop calling her the toady-faced mare and rename her the Wise One.

This night seemed so long without Jodie's silent ways and the dogs mulling around and without my nice warm and comfortable stable to lie in. Dawn started to break and still there was no sign of Jodie, the dogs or indeed the little boy, Si.

The newly named Wise One, the large bay, Half-Pint and the wee dark bay stuck closer together than usual, which seemed to confirm that something was up. Charlie Barnie seemed to hover between us all, which I took comfort from; but it wasn't the same as having Jodie around. Not that I would dare admit it.

The early morning hay and feed didn't appear either. Oh no! What's happened? A few hours later, though, Hob Nob came back with the dogs and another big bag of hay. She repeated her trick with the hay piles in the field, which of course Wise One went to without delay. I still stayed well away, though – I didn't want Hob Nob, I wanted Jodie! Perhaps she would be back later? But no, it was Hob Nob again! Oh no! What if Jodie never comes back! What will become of me? I know, I'll stick closer to Barnie, he'll make me feel safe – and perhaps I could try and get a bit closer to the big dark bay, whose name I think is Boxer. Maybe then the Wise One might accept me better. Or is she just, in a round about way, trying to teach me how to be a normal horse?

There were so many new thoughts going through my head!. Of course, I was always thinking about 'if' plans. But, you know, the two things that kept coming home to me were: 1) Nothing horrible has happened to me for the last few weeks and 2) the horses around me now are what I'd call 'safe' horses; so maybe, just maybe, there's the tiniest glimpse of a chance that I could become a safe horse too. Thoughts like that gave me a warm, reassuring tingle in my heart and made the hours without Jodie pass more quickly.

Daylight drew to dusk and dusk drew to dark but still no sign of Jodie. Even Hob Nob didn't appear and Wise One was clearly irritated. Then I heard a 'putt putt', 'putt putt putt' and Wise One lifted her head as a car pulled up with its lights on. She must have recognised the sound because she dashed down to the gate, giving a most welcoming whinny. A tin door banged, then: 'Hello Didget Doo!' said a wee quiet voice. The dogs' barks seemed filled with joy and even Ginger Beer ran fast and furiously down from the wood, where I hadn't even realised he had been hiding. Something positive was afoot! Sure enough all the lights in the barn and stables went on – YIPPEE, tea! I thought. But maybe not – I don't know this person. Maybe I should stay where I am till Jodie comes back. I'll see what the other horses do, especially *Wise One*.

A wee while later the field light went on and the small-voiced person, followed by the dogs, walked into the field down the ramp from the little dark bay's stable door. Mmm, all the horses, bar me of course, met her and demanded their own individual types of attention, which they got. If I had been deaf and blind, this could easily have been a mini version of Jodie – her approach was the same in every way. Maybe it would be safe to follow suit after all? I continued to watch.

Not long after, Little Voice appeared at the barn's field gate. Without a word or a whinny, Wise One and Half-Pint went in and the big bay called Boxer and my little buddy Charlie Barnie went next. Little Voice obviously knew the set-up, I thought. Perhaps she was Jodie in disguise!

By this time I had gently walked down towards the far side of the burn. Shortly afterwards, Little Voice appeared at my ramp, saying, 'Chessie, you stay there just now' (oh, so that's the little bay's name). She then opened the ramp door, walked to the side and kept completely still, using Jodie's language. It took me 45 minutes to find the confidence to go up the ramp, with Little Voice a good 12 metres away. Once I was in, Chessie followed instantly and went into his stable. *You know, the nicest thing about this was that it meant there were now, in all my years of existence, two people who had not rushed, harassed or forced me to do something but allowed me to do something in MY TIME.*

I remember years ago seeing an old, blind pony forced to do something at far too fast a pace for her and oh, the sheer panic on her face! I have never forgotten it. *Why are some humans always in such a rush, especially when it involves an ailing or elderly animal? If only one day they could be shown what it is like to be rushed when you have an illness or are stiff with age – perhaps they might give the sufferer a bit more time and patience.*

Anyway, eventually I was back in my stable with my two hay nets filled, my yellow feed bucket on the floor – with food in it, thankfully – and a bucket of fresh cold water at the back wall. It was so comforting to be back inside. Little Voice seemed to know all about the titbit, too, because later, when I went for my night-time wander, I found my usual Jodie midnight snack waiting for me. Jodie must have programmed Little Voice with all the dos and don'ts of the yard, because everything was running smoothly, even down to the number of lights she left on when she retired for the night.

Next morning there was still no sign of Jodie, but Little Voice seemed to manage everything without much of a to-do. I did have to tell her to go a bit slower when I was in the yard, though. And you know something? She actually listened. I was dumbstruck! This was the second person in my ten years of existence who had actually listened to my needs. The other horses seemed to like her ways as well. Yes, I reckoned I could cope with Little Voice for a few days – that was, if push came to shove. As it happened, push did come to shove and we didn't see Jodie for about a week. I was really worried, but I have to say Little Voice was really good to us.

A week later we were all down by the burn, grazing, when I heard Jodie's pick-up return. Did Wise One know Jodie was on her way home? Did the others know? Are they that in tune with her thoughts? I have never seen this before, but it certainly seemed that way. Anyway, Jodie jumped out of the pick-up, hared into her stable, dashed out to the field to check us all, gave THEM all a horsy scratch, almost as if to apologise, jogged the dogs round the field and hared back again to the pick-up with a bag in hand, started the engine, turned around and drove off again. When I thought about it later, she had seemed really sad. It was like the sadness I had when I lost my foals. Had she lost a loved one, maybe one of her family? Thinking about how loyal she had been with us and how well she had tended to my needs and with feeling her sad loss, I forgave her for being away for the whole week and was grateful to Little Voice for covering for her. I just hoped she would return soon.

For the next few days I accommodated Little Voice's requests, just as she did mine, but I wouldn't allow her to get as close as Jodie had managed. Still, it made such a pleasant change not to have always to be on my guard, worrying about what the next person was going to do to me. I truly began to feel I could shut down my eyes and ears at night time, instead of always having one open as a radar alarm!

The only thing that pulled me down sometimes, especially when I was in the stable on my own, was the thought of my foals. To cheer myself up I would wander into the yard to see

Charlie Barnie through the gate and nine times out of ten he would come up to muzzle me through the spars. And of course I had the painting of Billy Bob, with his kind eyes, looking down on me as I lay in my stable.

Little Voice continued to look after us for the next few days; feeding us, filling our hay nets to the brim and always refreshing our water. She was extremely patient with me, trying to understand my quirky ways. Wise One seemed a little forlorn – perhaps like me, she was missing Jodie. So when we heard the pick-up pulling up outside all our ears pricked up with delight – not that there was anything the matter with Little Voice of course.

Instead of Jodie going into her stable, she went straight in to see Wise One. I watched through the gate, to see her head hung low in silence against Wise One's neck. Something had definitely happened because for the next few days she seemed to be rushing around trying to organise something, and although we had our food and water all right and were let out into the field, she didn't spend her usual time or energy on us. She seemed to have extra silent time with Wise One, though.

From the field one morning I saw her dressed in black. The tall man Todd and the little person Si were looking very smart, and even the pick-up had had a wash! They drove off in it but were back later in the day. From then on it was as if something had closed within her, or a chapter in her book of life had drawn to a close. Although she was sad at times, I felt that deep down, she was okay with whatever had happened.

Our life with Jodie resumed as it was before her troubles. We were back on track. I still took hours each evening to pluck up the courage to have tea with her standing seven metres away.

A few days after she was back, before getting my tea, Jodie held something out in her hand, clearly hoping that I would take it. Although she stood perfectly still, though, her body language was wrong and I just couldn't risk it. She did the same thing for quite a number of days but I still didn't have the courage.

Each night, after declining her kind offer, I kept wondering how I could show her what it was I needed. First, she stood still with her palm open, but her left hand was crossed across her stomach, and that rang too many alarm bells with me. I was scared that my muzzle would be snatched and twitched. Her left hand, I thought, was going to grab me so that she could put something horrible round my neck like the strap that caused my terrible scarring. Jodie must have stood there for three hours one night, completely still, but this time it was a jammy doughnut in her hand – I couldn't resist it.

In total silence, she held a whole doughnut between the first finger and thumb of her right hand and kept it as outstretched as it could go. This time, she kept her left hand totally motionless by her side. She had understood me! I took a step forward; she didn't flinch, but I waited ten minutes just to make sure she wasn't going to move. Then another step forward and she still didn't move. One more step would allow me to stretch my neck to grab the doughnut then to run backwards, I thought. And YIPPEE, I got it! It was delicious. Should I dare go for another? Jodie moved back slowly to get another doughnut, which she held out to me just as before, and I bravely stepped forward for it – and this time I only reversed back two steps! I was beginning to feel braver and could have done with some more, but no more were to be had.

As a bravery reward Jodie brought out my yellow feed bucket, laid it on the ground and stood, this time only six metres away, again motionless. I couldn't stop thinking about how brave I had been – and grateful for how patient Jodie had been. Another first, and an extra titbit in my midnight snack bucket! Over time I managed to take something from her every night, but only on the condition that she stood still, completely still. If even a finger moved out of place I wouldn't go back for a few days; but perseverance on both our parts and a treat by hand, albeit an outstretched hand, became common practice.

Through the day I would be let out in the field with the others, where, once I had gained a bit of confidence, I could be seen frolicking around with Charlie Barnie, my tail held high with almost a cheeky swing to my body. I felt free, playing almost as if I was a youngster, enjoying those playful days I should have had but can't remember. Did I ever have them? Those black days overshadow any recollection of fun-filled times. Perhaps I can make up for those lost times one day.

With the green grass, hay, good food, doughnuts and other little treats, my girth was now quite definitely rounded, and my hooves no longer looked so cracked like broken slates. My hair no longer stood up on end and my eyes were beginning to twinkle – but I still had that tweezle in my mane. No one could touch me, I just wouldn't let them. I often saw Jodie scratching the other horses and so wanted to let her do the same on my white polar-bear coat. Deep down, my skin still ached and the memories of the physical and mental wounds were raw to the touch. Even Jodie didn't know just how badly damaged, physically and mentally, I was. So, until I could trust her to come close, my mane would stay tousled, and I would have to make do with scratching up against a door or a gatepost.

As spring moved into summer and the sun shone, my thick coat was almost out and my thin, cooler coat grew in. The stables had been hosed down from winter and everything seemed fresh.

Jodie decided that the stable I was in was too small for what she had in mind for me, so I was moved to a much bigger stable it was probably the size of three modern-day stables.

It was a bright place with all four walls painted white, and it had a high roof, a door at one end and one at the other, both at the same side. At the far right-hand corner there was a big round table, about four feet high and the same wide. It had a couple of brushes on it and something made of red plastic, that looked like an apple, dangling on a piece of rope. A long bench ran down the right-hand side as you went in, and wood shavings covered about a quarter of the floor, the rest being well-swept concrete.

At the top of the door at the far end was a metal grid, which led to Chessie's stable, and then to the concrete ramp leading towards the field. I had never gone in or indeed out of any of these doors before so was a bit uncertain of the whole thing. But, in the correct way for me, anyway – Jodie encouraged me in from the yard side. There was a hay net hanging up to the right side of the bottom door and one hanging up half-way along the corridor towards it. I was definitely happy! My previous stable only had one hanging point for a hay net, so to have two was a real bonus. A little like going to a restaurant and being offered seconds! The view out of the top door looked towards the top of the yard and into what was classified as the hay shed.

The latter was particularly precious to me. My memories of being starved of food and water, and then drinking only evil, black water, will never leave me. This water was like gold dust to me.

In my new stable I had to listen while the other horses ate their breakfast – I was always last to be fed. Then Jodie had a little routine geared up to try to encourage me to take something with her standing slightly closer to me.

The big round table that had what I realised was a molasses-dipped apple dangling from it was the place that this routine would start. The only titbits I responded to at this stage were either sticky doughnuts or bread – I guess that tells you a little bit about my past.

Jodie would walk in, at which point I would go to the far corner and pretend to fall asleep. Then she would walk very slowly and place a piece of my treat on the table, knock on the table twice, reverse right back to the stable door, stay absolutely motionless and wait, sometimes for half an hour, before I would pluck up the courage to go forward to take it. If she flinched at all I would jump back and not return for some time, so as you can imagine this often meant my breakfast didn't arrive for ages.

After about ten days of going through this long rigmarole, however, I finally plucked up the courage to take the apple when she was not quite so far away.

Chapter 17

Jodie's yard

'My new yard'

I MUST HAVE BEEN at Jodie's yard for about a month or so and by this stage, thanks to scrumptious food, doughnuts and bread my skin didn't feel as if it was pressing against my bony ribs, hips or my knife-shaped chest bone any more. In fact, I was beginning to see a rounded pot when I looked back, instead of just fresh air and a rack of ribs. I guess this might have been why I felt I had a bit more energy – positive energy, at that. I suppose you could equate it to a car: if you ran it dry or until it was low on fuel then it wouldn't go far either, nor would it sound particularly happy.

The other thing about Jodie's yard was the number of non-threatening people who came to visit. Most of them were interested to see all the animals, sheep included, but why they would want to see sheep is beyond me. They are wee, greedy and obnoxious, especially Charlie!

Other events that triggered my 'Black' memories

All these people would stroke or pat the other horses. I would have loved to be included but I was just too scared. Thankfully, Jodie knew this and always guided them to a point that she knew I could cope with. I hated the sound of my original name as much as I hated the sound of the other horses or dogs being patted. The phrase 'Good girl' to me was also a no-no, purely because in my past I would be called this and then battered. I could only cope with silence and absolutely no movement of any hand, finger, foot or face.

There were a few very wet days when Jodie wore a big long coat, I guess to keep herself dry – but as soon as I saw it, I bolted away to the other side of the stable and shivered. She took it off as soon as she realised that it had triggered another black memory. Then there

71

was the time the power went out at night and she had to use a torch – my memory bank couldn't cope with that either, so she very considerately turned it off. Once, her partner Todd had a wee fire in the wood, burning some rubbish – I completely freaked at that and stayed as far away from it as I could. And Jodie wore a red jacket one day, which again triggered a horrible memory.

Jodie and Todd's wee boy Si was a great little person and would come in with Jodie quite regularly. I liked him; he was small, non-threatening, at least until he scratched his nose or something, at which point I would rather have darted to the back of my stable than hurt him. I remember one day Jodie was in the stable with me and I heard Si cry. I was so concerned something had happened to him that I jumped to attention and wanted to get out to make sure he was okay. Jodie went to get him, but seemed to take ages to bring him in. I was so worried, but eventually she brought him in and he was okay. I was so relieved.

The other thing that concerned me, and still does, is the screeching or crying of other animals. Sometimes our neighbouring sheep, if they get stuck, start crying and this totally freaks me – again memories of sounds from my past. One evening I heard a young foal cry and it was awful; all the memories of screeching animals came flooding back. I wanted out, there and then. Jodie let me go, and I galloped off through the barn and out the gate to the top end of the field. Jodie following me, only to discover that a neighbouring foal had got stuck between two fences.

Then there was a really horrible wet day when we all, thankfully, stayed in. I could see from a distance that Jodie and Todd were braving the weather and doing something with the wee trailer – it was stuck, and they were linking up a chinking chain to their car. It was a terrifying sound and I dashed to the back of my stable and shivered. Jodie heard me and peered over, then asked Todd to put the chains down straight away. After that they used a silent rope instead.

If Jodie had forgotten to take a lead rope from her shoulder before walking into my stable I'd be at the corner or out before you could say boo to a goose. Or if, unbeknown to her, the same rope had fallen from her shoulder to the ground I would give it a wide berth because I was so scared it would end up round my legs.

If Jodie offered anything from the palm of her hand I would completely freak, thinking my muzzle was going to be caught and tied.

To touch me was like giving me an electric shock. To stand anywhere near me while I was eating either my hay or food or drinking water was an absolute no-go too, because I thought I was going to be collared, kicked or beaten. My thoughts had always been: 'How will I cope with all these horrible things happening to me? What else could they possibly do to hurt me, both physically and mentally?'

But I was beginning to find my thoughts slightly changing now: 'Will these positive experiences remain consistent – and, if so, how long is it going to take for my negative memories to be overpowered by positive ones?'

Jodie clearly had different plans for me, but I wasn't quite sure what. I was rather curious as to why I had been promoted to Wise One's stable – or was it in fact demotion? Was it Wise One's choice, being the favourite – at least, she seemed to me to be the favourite – or did Jodie think I had settled in enough that I wouldn't do any further damage to the yard? Yes, I'm afraid it was the latter; because, thinking about it, Jodie was extremely fair about dividing her time between each horse, including cheeky Half-Pint! Just seeing the horses being given some attention was enough to make me feel ten times more content than I had done for a long time, although the scars and black memories still hurt.

From this stable I could hear music, but very soft music, with deep relaxing breathing sounds or dolphins chattering in the background. With the combination of these soothing sounds and seeing the Wise One so relaxed I was beginning to feel a true sense of peace. Although there were times when I would stand or lie down, hanging my head low with my body sunken, but, Jodie clearly picked up on this and often used to sit with me for hours. I think she was trying her hardest to work out a way of cheering me up.

One evening I noticed her little black box letting out many elephant sounds. For most of these calls it was as if a normal conversation was going on, but as it got later there were more and more that seemed to leave her upset. In fact, she seemed as upset as I looked. Was there something going on? Was this change of stable bringing another change, perhaps for the worse? Or were her tears coming from me? I realised that my head started to lift a bit and eventually connected this with her tears and wondered whether she had a silent way of exchanging my sadness for happiness. But often the black memories of my past would come rushing back as fast as the mains water comes out of a fully turned-on tap.

Chapter 18
Things take a turn for the worse

'Eek! Why me?'

SURE ENOUGH, I thought everything had been too good to be true. All those conversations with the little black elephant box had been about Hob Nob wanting to sell me. I was no use to her the way I was, you see. Once again I was rejected. If only she could have understood what I had been through, she might have changed her mind. ***But instead I was being labelled USELESS – no good for what Hob Nob wanted me for.***

Jodie had clearly realised some of the things that had happened to me, from my reactions to experiences I had had while with her. As far as I could pick up from Jodie, selling me to someone was not an option. I think she tried to tell Hob Nob this and begged for a few more weeks to work with me, which Hob Nob initially agreed to. In the meantime, Jodie was obviously searching her brain for something else to try, but was clearly struggling.

I guess, to a point, I could understand. After all, I was only at Jodie's yard to be fixed. Jodie was clearly upset at the thought of me going anywhere, especially now she knew something of my miserable past. I guess, like me, she hoped that Hob Nob would agree to keeping me at her place for a bit longer, or at least until I was better.

Hob Nob kept contacting Jodie via the black box – rarely in person, though. She kept asking whether Jodie had thought of anyone who would want to buy me, but as Jodie said, it wouldn't be fair on either me or the other person unless they had a bucket full of patience.

Now, in between Jodie working on me she had the other five horses to look after and of course Si, not to mention the other things that she did – which included thumping away on that black thing with the big screen in her kitchen, looking after some elderly folk and talking to other people too, who seemed to come to her for guidance. So I guess it was stretching her to expect to be able to communicate how much I would actually much rather stay with her.

A couple of weeks went by without Hob Nob making roaring noises on Jodie's little black thing but then it all started again. This time, it was a thousand times worse! She was proposing to sell me to the Meat Man! Jodie looked distraught, and I was devastated. What was to become of me? How would they catch me, when I can't be caught? How would they transport me? How would they restrain me in the wagon? Where would I be transported to? How would they take me out of the wagon safely, when all I would want to do would be to run through whatever was in front of me? How would they restrain me to be culled? Would I be tied down by all fours again? How would they cull me? Would it be with a bullet from a distance? What if they missed or partly missed and I tried to run free with an aching bullet inside me? Or would they force me in to a cattle crush, stun me, or supposedly stun me, then bleed me alive? What heartless person would get the job! Would I end up giving out screeching cries for help like the other animals I had heard in the past?

I was already petrified – I wouldn't let anyone closer than 12 metres, never mind six I couldn't imagine my last few days of life. Because I was now a little on the plump side, would I get exported alive to somewhere like France? Would I be bled to death? My heart felt as if it had sunk to the bottom of the ocean. Humans had made me as scared as I am today and now they wanted to cull me!

If only humans had been just a bit more considerate to my ways and tried to understand me, I wouldn't be the way I am.

I often wonder if this is what some humans do to other humans who have been through such as I have, who have lost the power to communicate, or are confused because they are ill. Perhaps there are humans, like me, who have no one in their lives who will take time to communicate with them, or understand them. Do those humans feel the same way – neglected, rejected, useless and unloved by those who used to care?

What a cruel, cruel world we live in.

HOW SOME ANIMALS AND HUMANS FEEL

I am captured on the carousel of time
I don't understand the world around me
I feel so locked in
It's as if they think I cannot see
But I see more than her or him
I just don't know how to communicate with the world around me
I am captured on the carousel of time.

I over-react because I am misunderstood
My world is filled with anger and frustration
I so wish to show the world that I can be good
But the world doesn't seem to want a connection
I am fed up of rejection.

So few people give me the time of day
Maybe one in a hundred understand me
But the others push me out the way
How long is it going to take to make them see
I just need to be guided in the right way
I need time and the right key to unlock me
I want to feel free of this demon inside me.

Jodie was clearly in shock over the thought of sending me to the Meat Man. I could sense she couldn't believe anyone would want to do something like that, **especially when it was humans who had done all the damage in the first place**. I think she accepted that the meat market could be an option for certain animals but not for an abused animal like me.

'There must be an answer to this somewhere,' I heard her say. 'No animal should have to go across to the other side with such a fear of the human race, especially when they would have to be handled, and then put down, in what be, in this case, an inhumane way.'

One day, one of her friends came to visit and I could sense they were talking about me. 'Well,' her friend said, 'If she (meaning me) was to go down to Redwings it would be a very humane way to be put down. They take them out of the box, walk them into a stable, wait till they are eating out of a bucket and then BANG! Through the wall and it's lights out!'

But Jodie replied, 'Yes, that's okay for your normal, obedient, fearless horse, but with this one, who you can't even put a halter on, never mind walk with her into a stable. It's just not an option. In fact, I could well imagine her jumping out or over the people even before she got as far as their stable!'

Another time I heard her say, 'It is just not an option for this horse, when, **given time and the right understanding she could come right**.' 'But what's the point, if she can't be ridden?' the person who was talking to her said.

'Well,' said Jodie, 'I feel we should at least give her the chance, even although it may take time. At the very least she could be shown that all humans aren't horrible and that she could allow her trust in them to grow. After all, she has progressed, albeit just a wee fraction since she has been with us.'

Her friend said, 'Well, I guess it's more just a case that I know I wouldn't have the patience to sort such an animal.'

That time, Jodie went silent for a few moments before saying, 'I seriously think this horse in particular should be given a chance.'

At the end of the day, though, it was up to Hob Nob, because I belonged to her and not to Jodie. Not that Jodie gave up. She spoke to her vet and other horse-owning friends to see if there were any alternative, less threatening, methods of culling me. And she kept sending messages to Hob Nob, hoping for a clue as to how, when and where this potential cull would take place.

She was clearly trying her hardest to stand my ground for me, but was struggling for a conclusion to my worst ever nightmare.

My head and body hung low for days and my invisible tears were endless. Jodie was the same. I am sure she saw the potential in me and was gutted at the thought that Hob Nob could not stretch to giving me a chance, especially after all that I had been through. When it came down to mental and physical abuse, I am sure she thought I was the worst case ever.

In the meantime, Jodie kept giving me wonderful food, fresh water, hay (all of which I guzzled as if there was no tomorrow) and hours of time, in the hope that I might show her a few more glimpses of improvement. I tried so hard, to the point where I eventually let her touch my off side shoulder; but no way was I letting her close to my near side or indeed my face or the rest of my body, and her body had to be absolutely still, with not even a flick of a hair strand, otherwise I was off!

There was no word from Hob Nob for a few weeks. It was great; perhaps she had forgotten about me. But no, another message came through to say that she had spoken to the Meat Man and he would be in our area within three weeks.

If that's the way it was going to be, I thought, then I was dashed sure I was going to enjoy every bit of fresh air and care I had found.

Things were strange, though, because Jodie seemed to disappear quite a lot. Was she on a mission? Where did she go? In the evenings she would sit at my table writing things down. Were they my thoughts? Were they her thoughts? All I could sense was that she was trying her very best to find a way forward for me so that I could be given a chance.

She kept writing, then tearing the bits of paper up. What was it she was writing? After a few days of off-and-on writing she finally picked up two bits of written paper and took them away. For the next few days she would return looking weak, sad and drained. Then all of a sudden I could feel a hint of hope, her phone would ring and not just make the elephant sounds – the voices I could hear seemed positive and filled with ideas. I heard the word 'Sponsor' being mentioned.

I thought about it and guessed I wasn't that cheap a horse to feed or care for, but maybe, just maybe this was an option. In the meantime there seemed to be a lot of silent but positive energy coming my way. Where were these feelings coming from? Had someone started to wave a magic wand, or had someone put a prayer into a prayer box? Or had she spoken to people who had 'silent powers' that could alleviate dark thoughts? It was amazing! Over a period of three weeks I sensed there was a real ray of hope. More importantly, there was no word from Hob Nob. I really hoped that this time she had forgotten all about me.

I kept thinking about how Jodie had spent so much time with me and that she was the first person who had actually taken time to try to understand me fact I felt a bit like this:

At long last I have found someone

Who can turn my key
I feel free of the demon
When I am with them
For the first time
I can breathe, I feel free.

I have a chance to smile when I am with her
I have found what makes me happy,
For the first time ever I feel as if I am in heaven
I have laughed and smiled all day
And the devil inside me has run away.

Until now I had felt this:

So few people give me the time of day,
Maybe one in a hundred understand me
But the others push me out the way
How long is it going to take to make them see
I just need to be guided in the right way
I need time and the right key to unlock me

I want to feel free of this demon inside me.
Please, come share this happy day with me
And let me show you what turns my key
I so want to stop serving the devil inside me
But I need the world to show me the way.

I don't ask for much,
Just a little understanding, care and attention
I am fed up of rejection.

There's a lot of good inside me
But how long is it going to take
For the rest of the world to understand me?
I am tired, I am weary and I need a break
The demon inside controls me
I want to break free for ever
But I need the world to help me.
So, please, watch and listen
And that will help me.

Would I ever be given the chance to ask the rest of the world to help me? My Motto to date has been **'Don't give up'** and I will continue to stand by this with all hooves crossed.

During the next week or so I could feel nothing but positive energy but I had no idea where it was coming from. Was it all the people that had been introduced to me by Jodie who were sending me silent but positive feelings? Or was it just because there was more consistency in my life, which was making me feel less anxious?

I found myself assessing the last few months and thinking, 'For whatever reason Hob Nob was wanting rid of me – whether because of her lack of time, her commitments to more obedient horses or other things I didn't know about – I guess I should somehow try and thank her; after all, she did take me on in the first place and after a few weeks of good food and fresh water introduced me to Jodie. So, Hob Nob, just in case I don't see you again, and if you have the ability to pick up silent thoughts, here is a big thank-you for taking me on. Had you not, I would probably never have been given a chance to overcome my fears, or at least show someone that I just needed time to be understood.

But would I be allowed any more time? Was my time up?

Chapter 19
Where there's a will there's a way

'Take that!'

Tom Brodie

ONE AFTERNOON, we were all up in the field. Jodie was away; but a car pulled up and from a distance I half-recognised the lady's walk. With Jodie's car not being there I thought she would just drive off again, but no, I could see her speaking on her little black-buttoned thing and then she disappeared into Jodie's house and stayed there. As soon as Jodie returned, the lady dashed out to meet her and gave her a big hug! I thought, 'Oh, how I would so like to be hugged like that!' Would I ever be given the chance? Probably not.

They both jumped into the car and off they went. Mmm, how odd, I thought. Normally all friends and visitors come and say hello to the animals, including me – albeit from a distance. It wasn't long till they both returned and, yes, they came to see us all. From a distance, both their faces looked red raw, just like my heart often used to feel. Had they been crying? If so, was this the end of me?

Just at that moment Jodie's black box started trumpeting – oh, it's the elephants again! – and then I heard Jodie saying, 'The meat man is coming next Wednesday!'

I took the biggest GULP I had ever taken. My time is up, I'll be dead before I know it, I've had my chance and I've blown it!' I thought. But bizarrely enough, both Jodie and the other lady smiled. I was confused! Were they happy with the thought that I'd be turned into meat within the next few days?

As they got closer, I could hear them saying, 'Let's just text her back, shall we?' Again, they had smiles on their faces! Had they sorted something out, had they worked out a future for me? Had all the running around and silent thoughts paid off after all? Was I destined to stay here, in a secure environment where I would be given the chance to be me, or had they found somewhere else for me to go?

That evening confirmed everything. Jodie seemed completely at peace, more so than I had seen her since the words 'Meat Man' had been mentioned. It was as if she was trying to relay to me that I was safe. I had never had anyone stand up for me like this before; it was almost too good to be true.

But sure enough, as of the next day, when Hob Nob came down and picked something up from Jodie – it looked like a piece of paper with writing and numbers on it; a cheque, perhaps – I have never heard the words 'Meat Man' or 'She'll have to be sold!' again.

I guess part of me had hoped that Hob Nob would come to see me after she'd picked up the piece of paper, but no. So I have never had the chance to say a proper thank-you to her. Maybe one time!

From that day on my spirits lifted. I had been purchased, courtesy of donations! My name was changed to 'LAUDER LASS' and my future was now totally in the hands of the people who had supported and cared for me since coming to Jodie's yard. I will be forever in their debt.

That evening Jodie's little black box never seemed to stop trumpeting, and the sheer relief – for her and of course for me – was just tremendous. Perhaps, at long last, my climb to my 'MOUNT CONFIDENCE' can start.

Over the next few days Jodie was obviously thinking of serious ways forward for me, and one thing she came up with, to help rid me of my fear of humans, was to set up a Lauder Lass Visitors Diary. Mmm, not so sure about this one, I thought; but I guessed as long as Jodie was going to show people what I could cope with and what I couldn't, then that might be okay.

Chapter 20
Mountaintop moments

THERE WAS A real sense of relief around the yard which, after the threat of a 'Meat Man coming to take me away' was just awesome. But I still often thought of my five missing foals. This dragged me back down, as did the flashbacks and nightmares about my past.

A couple of nights later, something must have stirred in Jodie because, very quietly, she brought a plastic white chair in and rested it just inside the stable door. On it she laid a plastic box with things that looked like thin bits of wood and little pots of something. Perhaps it was feed! As soon as she left my stable I went to investigate. Yuk, it was coloured liquid stuff. The taste was horrible.

Hearing her footsteps coming back I quietly moved to the back of the stable and watched to see what she was going to do next. First, she laid a rug on the ground, knelt down and slowly picked up a plate, poured some coloured stuff on it, and pulled out a long piece of wood with what looked like a soft thing at the end. I watched with great interest! She stared at the wall for a while, holding a thing on a piece of string that seemed to swing round. Then, moments later, she started to paint an outline. I couldn't make head nor tail of it!

Because her back was to me I thought she wouldn't notice if I quietly took a pace forward. As I watched, an outline in black appeared! She changed the wooden thing to another one and popped it into another splodgy heap of mixed liquid, bent down and made another outline, but this time it was the same colour as a field full of beautiful, luscious, mouth-watering green grass. Well, I can tell you, when I sneaked over to test it out earlier it certainly hadn't tasted like grass! But whatever she was doing, it made me feel as if I was outside on a hot summer's day. It didn't take her long to complete the green gap between the outlines that she had started before. She stopped again, stared at the wall as if in deep contemplation, mixed up another few colours, and within the first black outline created additional outlines but in a yellowy-browny-red colour. She had left some sections totally white, though, which left me a bit perplexed.

By this time she was kind of half-standing and half-crouching – very selfish, I thought, because I couldn't see a dashed thing. I wondered whether she would notice if I moved forward a bit. I decided to go for it. By doing this I managed to see three-quarters of what she was doing, although I was keeping my good eye on the long thin wooden thing, in case it hit me.

When she had almost finished I couldn't believe what I saw. It was my foal, my brown and white colt foal! He looked exactly the same as he did when I saw him last, his little brown tail sticking up in the air, his long gangly brown and white legs with white socks at the bottom! He was trotting, with his brown and white head held high, just like mine was when I first galloped round the field here.

I couldn't believe what she had done for me. Without thinking about it, I moved forward another pace, to find myself just a pace away from Jodie. It was awesome; I could see my foal, mark for mark, star for star and sock for sock! How did she do that? How did she know what marks were where? Have I started to communicate with her just like Wise One does?

She obviously felt the colour needed tweaked a bit but I tell you, by the time she had finished it was hair for hair identical to my little colt foal. This was the first time I had seen one of my foals that I had dreamt of for all those years. I froze with warmth; I couldn't move. It was as if I was in the core of a dream – so much so that I didn't even notice Jodie leaving the stable. It was as if my hooves had been super-glued to the spot. I could feel my eyes softening with a nurturing instinct, an instinct I had never been given the chance to express. Never in my entire life had I been given the time to feel this experience without being harassed. The words **heart-rending** and **beautiful** aren't powerful enough for the emotions I felt.

By this time I found myself standing alongside my coloured foal, and was blocking the stable entrance in the process. Although I heard Jodie hovering in the background, I didn't know she was leaning against the stable door, watching me with a tear rolling down her cheek. My maternal instinct having come into play, I wasn't going to budge – not even for Jodie. I felt my whole body had risen a foot and seemed filled with pride and every muscle in my neck felt taut, my mane was tickling my shoulders – it was a feeling I hadn't felt since I gave birth to my last foal. I will hold that moment close to my heart for ever – to have my little colt standing at foot! My inner spirit was as elated as a human parent's would be, if their child had returned after being lost.

Jodie disappeared, then came back with my two hay nets – but she had to enter from the other end of the corridor. She must have sensed that I wasn't going to move to unblock the entrance for anyone. As she was tying one of the nets up she turned round to look at me. I hadn't moved and wasn't planning on moving, either. She must have sensed this because she moved one of the hay nets – very slowly and without making me flinch.

She reversed back, leant against the wall at the far end, rested a leg and just watched for a while. She wasn't a threat to my foal so I didn't mind. A good while later she left, but as she closed the door I caught her eye and blinked my eyes slowly, to say 'THANK YOU'.

 I wasn't leaving this foal's side for anything or anybody. I could reach my hay from where I was, so that was okay; and eventually I decided to lie down to rest a while. I lay next to my little colt foal and for the first time in a long while felt that life was worth living after all – a **Mountaintop Moment.**

The next morning Jodie did her usual rounds – dogs, sheep, geese, then us. But then there was mucking out. I had to contend with horrible things like a wheelbarrow, a fork, brush and shovel coming inside and having just regained my foal there was no way I was letting these tools anywhere near him, or indeed me. I blocked the entrance again, so Jodie had to use the other one. Eventually we all got some breakfast – bran, sugar beet, a barley free mix, some grass nuts and, to give it a wee bit of an extra bite – some fresh garlic – but this made my nose run! I guess it was a bit like a human blowing their nose after a curry or after brushing their teeth!

After breakfast, it was time to go out to the field as usual, but not having left by the bottom stable door before I was extremely reluctant to move, never mind move away from my beautiful colt foal. I had realised during the night that Colti didn't actually move, and that he was a bit like the dark bay, Billy Bob, painted on the wall in my old stable – a great comfort to me. So I was pretty sure he wouldn't disappear if I went out for a wee while; the problem was that with me blocking my usual door, and not wanting to try the other one, I couldn't get out!

Chapter 21
The threatening doorway

'I was too scared to go through'

THE DOOR AT the bottom of the stable was a lot narrower than the other gates at my new home. It must have been only four feet wide, and nine feet high. It opened out towards the left, where there was a white wall with a bright rainbow painted on it. To the right was another three-quarter sized wall with a stable at the other side. About three metres further on there was a gate to the left and then a half-sized wall straight ahead, in front of which there was a bucket on the ground. To the right of that wall was a wee corridor that led to a ramp and then the field.

Jodie opened the stable door and stood at the other side of the gate to the left. I walked towards the doorway, but as soon as I saw how narrow it was I froze. What would happen if I went through it? Would I be lassoed? Cornered? Captured? Was something going to jump out at me? Would I end up on another wagon? I truly didn't want to experience that again, especially not now that I was beginning to feel a bit more like a normal horse.

Jodie stood perfectly still while I vetted every brick in sight and every inch of the ground. Two hours later, and still unsure, I plucked up the courage to take a pace forward, then stood for another twenty minutes assessing every inch ahead.

Jodie stayed standing at the other side of the gate, but that reminded me of a past incident with a similar doorway, although a lot darker, where a man had been standing in her place; he was horrible and tried to capture me. All I could see was him, not Jodie, and I had to get out of there! Before I knew it, I had bolted past Jodie, turned sharp right, jumped the downward-sloping ramp and galloped across the stream, all within a matter of seconds! I stopped, looked round to make sure I was okay, and couldn't believe it! I was totally unharmed – and no one was chasing me!

As soon as Jodie saw me stop she slowly came into the field and walked parallel with me, although from a good 12 metres away. It was amazing. She didn't try to herd me back in, as others had done in the past. In fact she walked all the way round the field with me like this, stopping when I stopped and walking when I walked. I even gave a wee buck and a rear out of happiness and you know what? She copied me! It was wonderful.

A few hours later, spotting Jodie in the field with the dogs, I thought this was a way of getting back into the stables to check my foal. So I left the other horses to follow her – from a good distance away. I am sure she sensed what I was wanting, so she opened the ramp door – hoping, I guess, that I would go up it. She disappeared; I stood at the other side of the stream, aghast. No way was I going up that narrow corridor! Then I realised what she was doing, She opened up the field gate that led to the barn, the yard and the stables, came back down the ramp, gave me a wide berth but gently encouraged me in the gate. I only had one thing in mind – my colt foal – and I knew exactly where to find him. I aimed straight for my stable, turned round and stood beside him, gazing up towards the yard. From a considerate distance Jodie followed me, but no way could she enter my stable from that top door because I was standing protecting my foal, as my Mum had protected me. I was so contented that I didn't even touch my hay for the first half hour.

When I did eventually turn round to have a few strands of my hay I had another lovely surprise waiting for me – a chestnut filly foal, just like the one that was taken from me when she was only a few days old. I couldn't remember her quite so well, because I was with her such a very short time, but the pain I endured afterwards I remember still.

Jodie must have painted my new foal while I was out! It was just so heart-warming. That evening, I divided my time between my two foals, standing with one for a while, then the other. I even lay down in a totally different way to normal, with both foals in eye-shot, my head arched and my thoughts filled with pride. These happy-looking foals are mine and how proud I am! Thank you, Jodie.

I often wonder how she knew to paint these particular foals. All I knew at the time – although I wasn't going to show it – was that they were signs that someone truly cared for me.

Chapter 22

Visitors

AN EARLY VISITOR

BEFORE MY FIRST VISITOR arrived, Jodie changed my stable round a bit. She placed three chairs at the right-hand side for people to sit on – or perhaps it was just for putting my bread and doughnut treats on!

Before officially naming me **Lauder Lass,** Jodie had introduced people to me, so by this time I was sort of used to having two people in my stable at a time. But I only ever felt safe if Jodie was the one closest to me.

Since 21 July 2010, when the official Visitors Book opened for the first time, I have had numerous people coming to see me, all of whom have spent, on average, two hours at a time sitting beside me. They have all been extremely sensitive.

My first official **Lauder Lass** visitor, accompanied by Jodie of course, was a girl with short blonde hair and glasses. I think Jodie must have coached her as to how to enter my stable, which helped tremendously. I stayed in the furthest corner until I felt this new person (who had very kindly taken off her scary glasses) was safe, then – and then only – ventured over to take some of my hay, a safe six metres away from her. Jodie, leaving the blonde visitor sitting on the chair, calmly walked over towards the big round table, placed something on it, tapped the table, then reversed back to her seat. They both stayed absolutely still. After about ten minutes of assessing their movements I ventured over to the table to take what she had left. Mmm, it was a jammy doughnut! Scrumptious. I looked at Jodie and took a few paces back, hoping for another bit – and Jodie understood!

She placed another treat on the table and gave the table a couple of taps again. I went back for more.

The Blonde Girl then had a shot at putting something on the table, with Jodie's guidance of course. However, on her way over she flicked her hair. I jumped back as if I had been given another electric shock, which gave her a fright too; but she calmly said, 'I'm sorry,' and turned to look at Jodie for help.

'Keep going, and place it on the table, then slowly reverse back to your chair,' Jodie said. This she did; still, I felt I couldn't trust Miss Blonde without watching her for five minutes, to make sure she wasn't going to do it again. Eventually, gingerly, I retrieved my treat and looked at Jodie to ask for more. But she sent Blonde up again. This time there was no flicking of hair.

We went through the same routine again and again, but when I'd had eight doughnuts in total they seemed to think I had had enough – I couldn't see why! Then they started whispering to each other, clearly ignoring me. I felt safe enough to go for a mouthful or two of hay; everything was okay, at least until Blonde crossed one of her legs, which sent me flying to the other side of my stable. After about half an hour of them ignoring me, Jodie went to the table again and placed another treat on it and the familiar routine began again. Then it was Blonde's turn.

They stayed for another half hour and, quite frankly, I think I did very well, coping with a complete stranger – although, granted, we had no physical contact. They both left very quietly and had a wee blether in the yard before Blonde left.

'I had no idea how sensitive she was. I am so sorry I flicked my hair,' I could hear Blonde saying as they went. 'I never realised how threatening such movements could be – you assume all horses can cope with such little things. How wrong I was!'

Obviously my reactions to Blonde upset her, because I could feel her welling up inside as she started to say, 'The last thing I wanted to do to Lauder Lass was to startle her.'

'It's okay,' said Jodie. 'You didn't hurt her in any other way, so don't worry about it. She will be fine – and she needs to realise that little movements like that are not going to hurt her.'

MY SECOND OFFICIAL VISITOR

Gladness

At last, there's a hint of gladness,
With people filled with kindness.
I seem to have lost most of my sadness
Though memories of all the madness
Squeeze through in moments of quietness.

Anonymous

My next visitor was a lovely lady who seemed very calm, although she did have a habit of humming! She was, as always, accompanied by Jodie. I sensed she had had a lot to do with troubled horses and was very sensitive to my ways. Perhaps she ran an animal sanctuary or something. I felt that I had known her before but that may have been from hearing her voice on Jodie's little black box. She had a deep but soothing voice.

Jodie and this lady sat with me for ages, just watching, not threatening me in any way at all. It seemed that my visitor was truly shocked by my reactions to things. I heard her offer to speak to a friend of hers from Trinity in Sussex – a person who creates natural remedies for a wide variety of issues in both animals and humans – to see if there was a particular remedy that might help me. Mmm. On top of this, she said she'd speak to a healer to see what she could pick up.

Sure enough, a few weeks later, a natural remedy appeared. Apparently, it was similar to the medication they give to disturbed humans to help them overcome extreme anxiety and fear. It smells a bit like cider vinegar, with a hint of other unfamiliar smells, and is the same colour as treacle. Jodie seemed very grateful to the lady, but I don't think she's given me the remedy yet – I think she wants to see how I get on without any 'outside' help.

As for the lady visitor, she still comes to see me on a regular basis to check how I am progressing. I have since discovered that she does indeed run an animal sanctuary; it's called Mossburn Animal Centre, in Hightae, Lockerbie, Dumfries.

MY THIRD VISITOR

My next visitor arrived fairly early in the morning, just after the table routine had taken place and as I was about to be served breakfast. Jodie entered my stable first with my bucket and an elderly man followed behind her. I wasn't sure about this person, although he did smell a bit horsy! Jodie quietly ushered him to one of the seats on the right as you enter my stable, he sat down and watched me eat from about three metres away. But then Jodie cheated and slowly moved my bucket closer to them.

Well, the man was sitting silently, with his legs outstretched and his right arm crossed over towards his left side. Every time I put my head in the bucket I would give out my usual little squeal of uncertainty, and rightly so, because a little later he moved one of his fingers. I jumped back in alarm, and spent the next ten minutes assessing the situation before returning to my bucket.

'Oh dear, Jodie, what a case!' he said. 'I've never seen such a terrified horse; she has such a long way to go. I honestly don't think I would have the patience. Still, she has a kind eye.'

He seemed to look at my hooves a lot and mentioned that the raised lines indicated a very traumatised past with an exceptionally bad diet – although he said he could see that the hoof growing in at the top is smooth, so something has been right over the last couple of months. The man must have stayed with me for a good hour before he went off to do something to all the other horses. I have since learnt that he is a blacksmith, and one of the few that Jodie would have on the yard.

MY FOURTH VISITOR

This lady was small, softly spoken and introduced to me in the same way as the others. She was really moved by how scared I was of everything. I heard this visitor say, 'She is so gentle, and has such a kind eye. I don't understand how anyone could be so cruel to such an innocent animal. She did so well! Well done, Lauder Lass. Between us all you WILL get your confidence to be touched. I so hoped this would be the case, but time would tell.

MY FIFTH VISITOR

My fifth visitor was a lovely little lady, with dark hair and an amazing smile. She didn't say much, but I could feel her warmth; there was something extra special about her – I just couldn't quite put my hoof on what it was! She stayed for about an hour and a half and seemed full of understanding. This was a very special lady and one who I felt had something to do with some of the silent thoughts that had helped me to be where I am today. As time went on I discovered that she was in fact the minister at the local church. Funnily enough, she was called Frances. Jodie had mentioned to me that St Francis of Assisi was the patron saint of animals.

Chapter 23

A photographer comes to visit!

ALASTAIR WATSON

ALTHOUGH I WAS, or perhaps I should say, we, were all being visited by some lovely humans, there was one dark, damp mid-morning when the dogs barked abnormally.

Mmm, what was up? I heard Jodie outside talking to someone; sounded like a gentle-voiced man. About 15 minutes later Jodie appeared in the yard with this man who was carrying a three-legged thing on stilts. I believe it was called a tripod. He laid the tripod down and peeked over my stable door. Mmm, what was he up to, I wondered.

He called over to Jodie to ask her where her hat was, which seemed an odd request to me… But apparently he had seen her at various shows where she always wore her hat and now he wanted it in his picture. Maybe she should be called the Hat Lady after all?

The man asked Jodie to get me to stand right next to her at my stable door. Well, no way was I going to allow that to happen! But with gentle perseverance on Jodie's part – and great patience on the part of the photographer – and using the round table as a meeting place, an hour and a half later I found myself cautiously standing next to Jodie for the photo. In her folded hand, and hidden from view in the final photograph, was a little treat!

I don't think this man ever thought it would take so long to take a few photographs. But why did he need a photograph of me in the first place, I wondered? A couple of days later, when Jodie brought something over in a polythene cover and attached it to my door, I realised why: it was a newspaper article with that very photograph on it! Just imagine it! The **Southern Reporter** had given a whole page to my story! My goodness, I looked rather good, but Jodie looked awful. Thank you for being so patient and for telling my story, Mr Photographer!

Now Jodie and Si had to go away for a few days again but Jodie had organised for Little Voice to look after us. It was lovely to see her. And she left a lovely wee note in my dairy for Jodie's return.

'She is such a special horse; so nice natured and kind, just too scared,' the note said. 'Having spent the last four days with her, I have seen a noticeable improvement. She licked my hand today! She so wants to face her fears, she wants to be with you and when you sit quietly and still in her stable she really relaxes. There is definitely hope for her, I know she can do it.'

Shortly after Jodie returned from wherever she had had the audacity to go to, my regular visitors returned, and so did lots of new people, all of whom left some wonderful notes in my diary. There were a lot of them, but here are just a few:

'I cannot believe the transformation in this horse over the last few months. Long may it continue.'

'She's amazing and has taught me so much in such a short period of time, she's a gift given to us.'

'What this mare has been through is just crass cruelty, but what a joy to see her being able to relax her whole body and to take something from your hand without flying backwards thinking her muzzle was going to be snatched!'

'She's awesome, we must do everything we can to allow her to see that life here isn't that bad after all. I feel so at peace, sitting in the same room as her.'

'What a privilege to be able to share; she has taught me so much about myself, she's adorable.'

'How could anyone be so cruel to such an innocent animal? She's one of the saved ones.'

'I didn't have the chance to spend that much time with her earlier on this week, but today, she almost had her face right up to mine, I could feel the warmth of her breathing – it was magnificent. I just so wanted to touch her, but knew that if I did this she would bolt backwards. I need to teach myself to have more patience. It just makes you realise how threatening our actions are to anxious and scared individuals or how assuming we are when it comes to making contact with "tame" animals.'

'Thank you so much for having us over to see Lauder Lass and all your other lovely friends. We were really pleased to have been able to support you in helping Lauder Lass. She is so beautiful and so gentle. It's so good that Lauder Lass has come to such a caring place.'

'She so wants to please, but is just so scared to do so. She has a very kind eye and it's just wonderful to see and to feel her gaining confidence to take a step closer to you. The temptation to touch her is so great but I know this would just put her back.'

One very special visitor wrote:

'When sitting there listening to her, several comments became apparent; the most obvious, of course, being the brutal physical abuse that some humans had deliberately inflicted on her and her intense fear that other humans will do the same . . . For all that, underneath is a lovely person who desperately wishes to regain her trust in the human race. Then there is the mental trauma: this matriarchal mare has never been allowed to hold her rightful position among her own kind. However, the worst is the immense, excruciating sadness in having her children removed from her. This brings tears to your eyes. Jodie has done wonders for this horse and the more that people, who need have no knowledge of horses, visit her, the better. This mare is a healer and healing is a two-way transaction.'

Another visitor wrote:

'I think this horse does more for me than I do for her – she's fabulous.'

And one last one:

'I would never have believed that a horse, or anyone for that matter, would try so hard to regain their confidence – it's awesome. Every time she takes a step forward she makes me weak at my knees, I am so pleased to have been part of sharing these times with her.'

Chapter 24

I feel brave enough to make my television debut

'Feeling brave with ITV's Lee Maden'

A FORTNIGHT AFTER the article had been written about me I had more new visitors and I really began to feel that perhaps there was a chance that they might, given time, make my negative past become history. I was beginning to feel a lot braver. Jodie was even encouraging me to take things from all my visitors' hands ,' the note said. Although it was a slow process, starting with the ritual at the table, and it all depended on how each individual reacted. Their spare hand and body had to remain perfectly still, though.

Over time, if something spooked me, my visitors would only have to wait for five or ten minutes, instead of the previous 20, before I returned to the table from the far corner of my stable. I was really touched that all these people should choose to spend a minimum of two hours with me.

I was also beginning to trust Jodie in an open field. She could walk along side me, albeit from three metres away; this would have been unheard-of three months earlier. I had even started to take something from her hand without the use of the table. But I could still only do this if she was standing on my right side; my left side was still a no-go area. I would even, especially on a rainy day, follow her back to the stable (unlike the others I couldn't cope with a rug on my back, you see). I knew that was my only chance of staying dry and not being soaked to the skin so I wasn't going to miss out on that one!

One late morning I was called in from the field. As always, my hay net was filled and of course my water bucket had been refreshed. But at the far entrance, beside the door and two metres back from my colt foal was a man, and a long thin thing on three legs – another tripod! – with a camera at the top and a thing on a wee boom that looked like a hairy teapot or a hairy hedgehog at the end. I started eating my hay, keeping a sharp eye on the man and the hedgehog, but it was clear that Jodie had told him what he could do and what he couldn't. He didn't say much to start with, so I could cope with that, and then he asked if some other people could be in the stable with me so that he could film them with me, and possibly, if my body language allowed, interview them at the same time.

I already had three visitors waiting to see me. One was a little girl called Chloë, aged about nine, then there was a boy called Ian, aged 10, and a lady, who had been the first person to see me, called Katy (Blonde). Jodie gave the cameraman strict instructions not to move, then she slowly walked towards my bottom stable door and called the three visitors in. She gave them strict instructions, too: to walk slowly, to stop whenever she did, and to always stick together as if they were all one person. Well, I was used to two or three people being in my stable by now, but I had never had five in at one time. Jodie brought them in, checking first for signs that I was feeling safe. She showed them to their seats, on the left-hand side of the cameraman, although little Chloë had to stand. I didn't mind about that because she was quite a tiny person with a very friendly aura.

After letting them all pass, I returned to my hay and heard Katy saying she couldn't believe how much I had come on since the first time she saw me. She kept looking at Jodie, full of emotion. Little Chloë broke down, just standing in my stable next to me, albeit four metres away. Were my past tears coming through her, I wondered? She had such a kind little face with caring eyes; I didn't like seeing her upset, though. Ian sat beautifully, as if he sensed something magical within me. Then, sensing I was calm, Jodie said to the cameraman that it would be okay for him to talk quietly to my visitors while he was filming. He totally respected this and stopped talking when I flinched, for whatever reason.

Jodie started by placing a treat on the table, then following with the table taps. I was okay with this, but you know, I was really feeling for little Chloë; she was such a sweet little girl. I really wanted her trickling tears to stop. I think Jodie sensed this as well, so she went behind her and placed a treat in Chloë's hand, placed her hand underneath Chloë's and held it out in my direction. They both kept totally still. I had a real feeling of empathy for Chloë and took it very gently so that she wouldn't be hurt or get a fright – in the hope, even, that she would smile. Well, her whole face lit up! It was like a welcoming beacon on a far horizon. I could sense she wanted to jump with joy, but she knew I couldn't have coped with that – but her tears stopped immediately. I felt so proud that I could help such a small, fragile-looking person.

Afterwards she seemed to stand in complete shock that I had actually taken something from her. She still had that huge smile on her face, though, so I was happy. The next person in line, although sitting, was Ian; he wasn't so far off five feet tall and he had dark gingery hair. I had been watching him from the side of my eye, just as I had everyone else, and he seemed patient and kind as well. Unlike a lot of boys, he spoke very softly and had a wonderful twinkle in his eye. It was obvious he had watched what Jodie had done with Chloë so when it was time for him to give me a wee treat he did exactly the same. I felt a real empathy with this boy as well, but it was slightly different to the feeling I had for Chloë. Could it have been a loss of some sort? I thought I would be brave, just like I think he had had to be in his past, so I nudged him for another bit and then another. He smiled with sheer delight and with a true sparkle in his eyes.

Last in the queue was Katie, the lady who had helped Jodie find ways to keep me alive instead of becoming a steak on a plate. She was just tremendous with me and as a silent thank-you – and having pulled on my bravery hat courtesy of Ian I kept nudging her for more as well. More to the point, she obliged.

While she was giving me my extra treats, the cameraman was interviewing her, and the words she quietly uttered were: 'I can't believe she has come on so well. She's awesome! Well done, Lauder Lass,'

'You can do it,' she added. 'We are all here for you.' It really pulled my heartstrings to hear her say this.

This interview must have taken about two hours and although I sensed it was nearly finished, the cameraman wanted a closer picture. Mmm, not with that hairy hedgehog on a boom, I thought! Again, Jodie sensed this. Did he want to see if I would take something from him? It took her a few moments to work out where the equipment was going to be placed but I did it, I actually did take something from him! I had to have a couple of goes, though, because the hairy hedgehog on a stick wobbled every so often.

Jodie felt I had worked well enough, I think, so as a reward she let me out into the field. And, you know, for the first time I went out of my stable, straight out the door, down the ramp, without any fearful stops, and jumped over the stream, as if to say, I AM FINALLY SAFE! YIPPEE!

Jodie and the cameraman followed me up the field, talking quietly. It was during this conversation that I finally understood why I had such empathy for Ian. This was the first time he had been anywhere near a horse since his mother, Fiona, had been thrown from one and tragically died. I think she is a huge loss to all, but I felt, through Ian, that she would have had so much empathy for my situation – and been so proud of Ian sitting so patiently with me.

After the cameraman had left, Chloë wanted to spend some more time with me, but in the field this time. So Jodie brought her up. At this stage I was still keeping a safe distance away from the other horses (apart from Charlie Barnie, of course) so, I could often be seen standing on my own, munching away. I had already realised that I could take something from Jodie in the field (as long as her body language was right, that is) but I had never plucked up the courage to take anything from anyone else. Like Jodie, I could feel Chloë's wish to make contact with me; and I felt that as she had worked so hard with me in my stable, especially being such a fragile wee soul, I should make my biggest effort. Lo and behold, 40 minutes later, with guidance from Jodie, I did it – and made the little girl's day once again. I believe Jodie thought it was a momentous step forward for me. Perhaps she could encourage me to speak to others when I was in a large open space.

A GLOWING ANGEL

She stood there like a glowing angel
Looking oh so fresh and fair,
As we drew closer to tend and care
She bolted fast like on fresh air

Her body scarred through hate and money
I stood there silently and wept
How could people have done this and slept?
I wonder if, with constant patience
You will ever try to trust again!

Written by :
Helen and Chloë Paterson aged 10, Edinburgh

For some bizarre reason, this day confirmed my feeling that I was safe – and what a tremendous feeling it was! I will never forget it.

Well, that night I hit the news. The lady reporter, in particular, seemed very sympathetic towards my case. I'd like to thank her myself, one day, for her words of kindness, but maybe in the meantime she will read this book. So I'll say it here: 'THANK YOU FOR YOUR KIND WORDS, LADY REPORTER!'

Chapter 25

My Diary

BECAUSE OF THE number of visitors I was having, courtesy of the article in the *Southern Reporter* and my television debut, a diary was created and updated regularly and placed in local stores and on the dais in the local church for all interested parties to read.

The support from everyone was tremendous and introduced me to a totally different side of human nature. There are people up and down the land, from Wick to Devon and right across to New Zealand, who showed and still show great kindness towards me.

One lovely lady called Elaine came down from Edinburgh and spent ages with me. She even produced a painting which has been made into posters and cards (the latter were courtesy of Norma and Joan), the proceeds from which have gone towards my feed and bedding. She also painted a lovely painting of Charlie Barnie, my adopted son (photographs can be seen on page 57).

Ian from the other side of Kelso offered me hay through the winter, which was a great help, but more to the point it didn't have a speck of dust in it – thank you, Ian.

Jodie was offered a pitch at the two-day event at The Dogs Allowed Show at Thirlestane Castle in the middle of August in return for some dog behavioural sessions and judging. I gather Jodie found this to be quite difficult, as all the dogs that attended the Under One-year-old and Dog Most Like Its Owner class were superb. However, choices had to be made and I think she hopes those that did not win understood why.

Also at the show, Jodie, Alice and Josie ran an art and poetry for kids corner, and there were prizes for the best drawings. All proceeds from the day again went towards my winter's keep. A big thank-you to Ross and Hazel for inviting Jodie to the event. Maybe one year I will have the confidence to join them!

Chapter 26

Lauder Lass's progress

'Feeling happier'   Becky Leigh

28 AUGUST 2010

For those of you who have already visited me you will know the set-up and the way Jodie starts working with me. For those of you who don't, perhaps I can describe the introduction to my 'working hours'.

I have progressed from taking five hours to take something from you (and even this was only done if your spare hand was well out of the way and if you stood perfectly still) and running away from you in the field to now being guided towards my stable, but more often than not I follow the leader in (this being either Jodie or another confident visitor). I proceed up the field ramp, through a slight corridor then into my stable. I then start to eat some, previously soaked hay. Jodie then invites the visitors into my space, at which point I very kindly reverse three or four feet to let them by and onward to their seats that are placed at the top end of the stable beside a table where fruit and veg can be chopped up or soaked in treacle – mmm! (I used to reverse back to about three metres, would shiver in a corner and not eat my hay or any titbit until everyone was completely out of my stable.)

To the right of the seats there is an additional table that is the 'half-way house' meeting place where Jodie used to knock twice to encourage me over from my hay to eat whatever delicacy was on offer and then would reverse back to the seat very slowly so that she/they wouldn't startle me – a very easy thing to do, especially at the beginning.

The next step forward was to stretch me by taking something slightly closer to the individual, who had to sit motionless for about ten minutes before I felt safe enough to take any form of treat. Then this progressed to taking something closer towards the heads and faces of individuals, then closer to two people then between two people, then I progressed to allowing one person to stand beside the 'meeting table' but again they had to stand totally motionless otherwise I would fly backward – this still happens on occasions but it's not usually my fault, it's usually because of a sudden finger movement or a flick of the hair that has given me the fear to jump backwards.

Over recent weeks and till this day in August I am still encouraged to the initial round table as a meeting place but I am beginning to realise that this isn't such a scary experience after all and am beginning to feel confident enough to assess you for two minutes then come to you for my treat – this is terrific and all thanks to the amount of calming visitors who have had or have the patience for me.

In the field I have progressed from running away from you and other horses to taking something from your hand – this was experienced by one of my visitors on 9 August– a fantastic leap forward. I have also been accepted into the existing herd of horses, which I think is the first time I have had the chance of being a herd animal in all of my ten years of life. One of my visitors watched me frolicking with some of the other horses the other day. *'Aw, isn't that lovely to see, she wouldn't have dreamt of doing such a thing in her early days,'* she said. Another person watched me playing and running with Jodie in the field: *"We loved seeing her gallop over to HER place in HER field – no hesitation, appearing confident to be with the herd, and to see her respond to the invite to run with Jodie – just made the heart sing. It seems to me that she holds herself with a lift to the head now and she has filled out in her muscles and lovely curvy bum!!!"*

On 16 August, after the usual routine with the table knocking, I had the confidence to bring my head round your left shoulder to see what was in your hand and almost pushed you round so that my face was close up to your heart. On 23 August I stretched to cope with being stroked under my chin before being given any titbit (a major step forward) – initially I flew backwards a few times but, I came round to accepting it, that was as long as your body language was slow and non- threatening.

So, all in all, Jodie thinks I am doing remarkably well and that it's a joy to see and share my confidence growing for the first time in goodness knows how long. However, in saying this I still have a long way to go but we are all sure, with the help of all my visitors, that I will make it. Thank you everyone and keep up your silent thoughts and visits. Keep lighting those candles for me . . .

At the end of this section was a close-up picture of my head and the following words: "Thank you to all the people who have visited and keep visiting me on a regular basis. Your visits are helping me to overcome my fears of the human race and your support, albeit silent, material or indeed financial are all helping me towards a healthier and happier future."

Underneath was a copy of all the things that people had written on my stable door of which here are a few:

"It has been such a moving experience to sit with Lauder Lass, well done for the progress" P

"She's amazing and has taught me so much in such a short period of time, she's a gift given to us" J

"She so wants to please but is just so scared to do so" A

"What a privilege to be able to share, she has taught me so much about myself"

"She is so gentle and has such a kind eye, I don't understand how anyone could be so cruel to such an innocent animal"

"I cannot believe the transformation in this horse, long may it continue" Mo

"What a lucky girl, to be given a second chance" M

"How could anyone be so cruel to such an innocent animal, let's keep her safe" John

"Between us all you will get your confidence to be touched" Emma

"She has made me realise how threatening our actions and voices can be to anxious individuals" Kate

"She so wants to face her fears, she so wants to be with you" Mae

"How assuming we are when it comes to touching animals" Shae

"An amazing experience well done Lauder Lass, you can do it" Ian

"Well done, what a beautiful horse and a touching story to report" Lee

"What this mare has been through is just crass cruelty, but what a joy to see her beginning to relax her whole body and to be able to take something from your hand without flying backwards thinking her muzzle is going to be snatched is just tremendous" L

A comment from Bill and Sue:

There is one gentleman I can clearly remember; in fact, although elderly he still comes back to see me.

The first time I saw him was with Jodie. She had called me in, to which, by this stage, I responded immediately and he was sitting on the white chair beside the door waiting patiently. As always there was a lovely hay net waiting to be devoured so I started to munch away. Jodie stood by Bill and they both chatted away softly. He had such a soft tone about his voice, although I suspected, by the way he sat, at some stage in his past, he might have been quite a determined kind of a character and that something had perhaps happened to make him the way he is now! But all I knew was 'what I saw and heard I liked'. I felt he perhaps reciprocated this feeling because he said, 'she's got such a kind eye' and 'who could be so cruel to such a beautiful creature. However, it seemed his leg got a bit stiff because he seemed to move it quite regularly but it moved in a gentle and non-threatening way, so I didn't feel fazed at all.

As always Jodie encourages all, who are fit enough any way, to make contact with me. So, after enticing me over she asked Bill to stand and then she positioned him next to her. Her hand gently eased his right hand out towards me, and as soon as I made contact she encouraged his left hand to stroke my neck. Although he had very cold hands, which generally I would have reacted to, there was something special about his touch that made me want to stay with him, if he stopped I would give him a very gently nudge with my muzzle or move my neck closer to him. He seemed so sympathetic towards my needs, I often wondered and still often wonder why, has he gone through something similar or does he feel the same as I have done in my past; ousted, bullied, domineered or rejected. Or is it just that, like me, he appreciates being surrounded by 'kind hearted people' or those who can give us the time of day!

From another lady visitor:
It is a winter's night and very cold. The stars are twinkling in their millions up in the dark sky and I am glad to be sheltering in the stable, out of the wind, sitting in state on the cushion covered visitors bench. It is cosy inside and it feels like the night ahead is endless. Jodie never rushes us.

Lauder Lass is standing at her hay net, tugging mouthfuls and eating slowly and peacefully. I love the sound of a horse eating. Her stable feels like a sanctuary and I thank her for letting me share her private space.

I watch her for a while and then I slowly stretch out on the bench and lie there thinking about things almost in a meditative way. Lauder Lass is turning away from her hay net and walking in a purposeful circle then she folds herself down and is lying near me. I can hardly believe my eyes. It is magic! She trusts me enough to do this and I feel immeasurably honoured. Life has scarred her mind and body but she is still so gentle and beautiful. I love her. I feel safe lying there with her in the dark. Maybe I am one of her lost foals.

"She's a spokesperson for other horses, she's more powerful than you think and truly deserves to be given a chance to feel safe."

Chapter 27

September 2010 - December 2010

'What a relief.'   *Kate Oliphant*

I HAVE BEEN overwhelmed by all your visits and by all your treats, especially the huge sandwich that Mae and Shae made up for me. You should have seen them! They were like a triple decker bus with bread, chopped-up cabbage, carrots and molasses inside. I could hardly get my mouth round them. I am not sure that Jodie fully appreciated me having them, because as far as she is concerned treats are to be given in small quantities and only on a part-reward basis.

Of course, I can't forget about all the scrumptious doughnuts, brown bread, white bread, cakes and cookies that I've had from you all, either.

As time has gone on I've discovered I do like carrots and apples, even though to start with I turned my nose up at them. Or was it just because I didn't know what they were, or because I didn't know how to take them from you?

L and M were extremely generous, bringing me big bags of carrots, and as I became more confident with their presence I can remember, extremely cautiously, placing my head between them and L saying, with a grin the same size as a Cheshire cat's, 'she touched me' as a tear rolled down her cheek. This was the first day I dared go between two people. It was awesome, they didn't hurt me, or try to grab me, or make any sudden movements. Mind you, I suppose by this time I had become carrot-minded, and L and M had very deviously placed the carrots behind them – Jodie's idea I guess! One thing is for sure: Jodie always has me 'mentally' working. I sometimes wondered whether she would ever stop making me work! But I guess I might not have progressed so well had she not.

One afternoon L and M had arranged to visit but L pulled out at the last minute because of her knee problems, and M came along instead. By now I was getting used to my regulars and instead of looking at their body language I would be looking at the size of MY goody bag – *perhaps a bit like a grandchild does when their grandparents come to visit!*

Well, this particular day my confidence had obviously risen again because rather than giving M the chance to walk to her place in my stable I was almost right in her face before she had taken five steps forward. Now, according to Jodie, *this 'in the face' behaviour wasn't allowed.* She *calmly asked me to reverse,* but not being particularly chuffed at this I pulled one ear back – at which M said, with a lovely smile on her face, 'She's getting cheeky, uh!'

I really wanted to see what was in the bag, so just to surprise them both, I quietly sauntered up, placed myself between them, nudged Jodie out of the way a bit, muzzled the bag and ran to the back of my stable with this 'unexpectedly' noisy bag in my mouth. I thought the rustling sound was going to eat me up and I didn't know what to do with it. The carrots took a flyer, bouncing off me, the walls, the wooden plank! Eventually I used my brain and placed it gently on the ground – but blow me, by the time I had laid it down there wasn't a carrot left! Instead, all of the carrots were strewn all over my stable floor and covered in shavings! Well, I was extremely disgruntled, because everyone to date had spoilt me by washing the carrots before they arrived so I only ever ate clean carrots. What a transformation from three months ago, I thought!

After all of the carrots – there must have been 60 of them – had been retrieved and some eaten in the process (being cleaned first though) I decided to go and have a munch of my hay, to help the digestion of course. At the same time I was thinking how kind M had been over the past number of months. After all, both she and L had been so regular with their visits. Maybe I should show her a little extra form of appreciation? I wondered for a moment how I could do this.

Over the past few weeks I had allowed Jodie to stroke me a little further back than my withers and in fact had let her run her hand down the middle of my neck to just between my front legs. I wondered if I should try and trust someone else to do the same, and if so, M or L would be the best candidates for my experiment. So, as a kind of apology for my cheek, I slowly ventured up to M. She already knew the game – I let her touch me, then I get a treat, fairly simple, but could I let her stroke me any further back? I often heard Jodie saying, 'It'll be all right, you'll see,' so I thought I'd say that to myself: 'It'll be all right, you'll see,' over and over in my head, and I might in fact be okay! Well, I completely shocked myself by allowing M to stroke me for ages along my neck, down the front of my neck and right along my back, at least to the point where my 'somewhat large' rump started. Was it because I was concentrating so much on repeating 'It'll be alright, you'll see', 'It'll be alright, you'll see', 'It'll be alright, you'll see'? I don't think I had ever seen M's face shine like that light on a distant horizon before, like little Chloë's had done a few weeks before!

Deep down, I was beginning to enjoy making people happy, instead of having them always trying to make me happy. It was beginning to feel like a two-way communication on a deep and silent level. Some say it's like a dolphin swimming with you under water – magical, or perhaps even euphoric.

Never in a month of Sundays had I dreamt that my life could take such a turn for the better. I feel eternally grateful.

By now, instead of thinking *life was a bed of extremely sore gorse bushes, I was beginning to think of it as a bit like a bed of roses – beautifully coloured and scented but with thorns. Those thorns not only hurt; they stir up bad memories. But I was learning that by silently sharing those hurts with others, I could find a way to overcome the pain and pull out those sore thorns for good!*

I remember another visitor; he seemed full of himself and wasn't really interested in me at all. In fact to start with, he seemed to talk about himself all the time, with little care for how I might react to his twitchy, nervous body language. Not that he seemed nervous of me, though! The only thing he said that related to me was, 'When will she get a saddle on her back?' Is that all he cared about, I thought? Is that all he thinks horses are for? But sensing my unease Jodie silently stood in a way that felt non-threatening to me, as she replied with perfectly logical – to him – statements.

There was another thing that I found to be very odd about this man. Unlike all the other visitors, he couldn't look Jodie in the eye! Even one of the dogs felt uneasy with his presence. There must be a reason for the dog's and my anxiety, I thought, and now, with the benefit of hindsight, I wonder if Jodie realised there was something adrift.

He wasn't interested in giving me anything by hand or having any form of contact with me. An odd visitor: I'd need to feel more comfortable with him, or his 'hidden self', before I trusted him.

The next day a lovely lady and gentleman came to see me. They were sweet and spent ages with me, in fact they must have been in my stable for a whole afternoon. Jodie, as always, guided them to the way that I could accept contact and I welcomed their treats between each stroke. They also bought some of the cards that Norma had made; perhaps they were going to send them off to friends. The lady's husband was extremely soft and caring and made me forget about the unpleasant visitor I had had the day before. I think they also left some funding for my feed and bedding – how kind and thoughtful.

Mae and Shae returned regularly, bringing lots of treats like tins of treacle, chopped-up carrots, apples and bread all neatly cut into soldiers. I was growing fond of these two. Mae was softly spoken and, in her own quiet way, knew exactly what I was thinking. I think she must have an extra sense about her that all animals can connect with. Shae was tall and dark and, like Mae, had something special about her. I can specifically remember her third visit when I finally plucked up the courage to allow her to make contact with me. She said she would never wash the coat she had on again because she was so moved that it had MY hair on it! Bless her.

Another lovely couple came to see me. They said they thought I was adorable and just couldn't understand how anyone could have been so cruel to me, or any animal. They brought some wonderful treats, all of which were consumed in short order – my confidence had grown, you see. The lady, Joan, took quite a few photographs, one being a fantastic picture of Charlie Barnie, Jodie and me which ended up on a calendar that Jodie created at Christmas. Shortly after their visit, a huge envelope appeared with some more unusual cards, which, again, were to be used for fundraising purposes.

At the back end of September there must have been something planned because my stable suddenly had two extra four-seated wooden benches in it, just behind the large round table. I decided I didn't want to miss out on anything so I was quite stubborn about going out for a couple of mornings. Sure enough, a few days later, I heard a car arriving and not long after Jodie arrived with a man and a young lady, Although I didn't recognise the girl I did recognise the man from a previous visit. I remembered I liked his approach, although the pitch of his voice was a bit threatening. Another car pulled up, so Jodie asked the man and girl to stay calm – which may I just say, at this stage, they did. Jodie returned with another two people, but this time they entered from the yard and were calmly ushered to a bench. Not minutes later another car and yet another car pulled up and all the people were gently shown to their seats. Jodie seemed unfazed by it all, which helped me to cope with having 11 people in my stable at one time. I couldn't believe I was in a stable with this many people!

This was an extremely powerful day. Each of my visitors seemed to send me different strengths of silent thought and energy. Jodie introduced each of them individually, exactly as she had done all my other visitors. I reacted well to them all, although there was one very kind gentleman who I felt could give me only material things, not inner strength. Was this because that was what his life to date had encouraged him to do – give to others? Or was this how he had learnt to get something himself, by giving freely all the time? Perhaps by not allowing anyone to give him anything he was starving himself of genuine love and care? I would have liked to spend more time with him; but everyone else wanted to give me some of their hands-on energy, so we ran out of time.

Positive energy was in abundance that day. Thank you all so much for travelling such distances to spend time with me, and for the time you have spent on me subsequently.

There was another man who had read the article but because of his work and family commitments couldn't visit immediately. However, he eventually came and was so understanding of my situation. He even brought me some sticky buns and still sends me regular emails. I'm sorry he doesn't live in Scotland – I'd like to see him again.

In the United Kingdom, my most remote fans are from Devon and Wick. Let me describe them to you. Alice and Josie are from Devon. Alice is tall and Josie quite the opposite, in fact they are total opposites, Alice is the calm and collected one and Josie is completely dotty, in a friendly way. I had an immediate connection with Alice; it is a wonderful, heart-warming feeling when I meet this type of person – a true connection. Josie was wonderful as well but I felt I had to gently teach her a lesson or two before I could find the confidence to take anything from her. She had what I'd call *'ants in the pants'* so I had to make her aware of how fidgety she was. During her first hour with me I jolted in response to each flick of her fingers or toes, until she suddenly said to Alice, *'I don't think I have ever sat as still as this in my whole entire life!'* Jodie said, 'But my dear, *according to Lauder Lass you are not sitting still – watch how she reacts and connect it with your twitches!'* Perhaps she finds it difficult to be still for long periods of time, *like a horse fed on nothing but oats, or a child who drinks nothing but blackcurrant juice!* I was quick to teach her, though – or was it that she was a quick learner? Because she, like Alice, desperately wanted to make contact with me. Alice and Josie stayed for a whole week, which was wonderful. Often Josie would wonder where Alice had disappeared to, but guess where she was. Yes, that's right, either in the field or in my stable, keeping me company. Josie was a bit like Ginger Beer, the cat who still comes and sleeps on my big turquoise rug on the long white bench in my stable. Actually, I think Josie is more of a cat person than a 'me' person, but I'm okay with that, especially when Alice is around.

Now to my Wick connection called Danny and Co. Actually, they stay in Dunbeath, which is slightly south of Wick. Danny has a lot of respect for my recently found bravery, and was very sensitive to my story and the poem called 'How some Animals and Humans feel'. Perhaps Danny and Co have had dealings with humans with such issues in the past? However it is, I know they support me every step of the way and are delighted that I have been given a second chance.

'I am so inspired by what is going on with Lauder Lass, I pray that she survives the ordeal of change that she is going through and accepts the changes that will change her life,' Danny wrote to Jodie one day. *'As humans, what gives us the right to do what we do? We should all be ashamed of ourselves. I pray for Lauder Lass – may God give you the strength to see her through.'*

Chapter 28

Bravery

'Beginning to feel confident'

BY SEPTEMBER I had found a whole new confidence in the way I interacted with the other horses. Bones of contention were evened out and I, for once, began to have a say in where I wanted to be in the field. I no longer had that horrible feeling of being ousted or dominated, although I think I will always respect Wise One!

Now, Jodie often walked out in to the field with us in the mornings, almost as if she was another horse. We would all have a bit of a roll and often a wee frolic afterwards. Sometimes she would come out in the afternoon and spend time with me as I was grazing or just wandering around. Often I could even be seen standing next to her, allowing her to stroke my off side at the same time – an unheard of vision a few months ago!

But I can remember one afternoon as plain as day. As Jodie often did, she came out to join us all but we were having twenty winks, lying down next to our buddies – Wise One with Boxer, Ralphi between them and Chessie and faithful Charlie Barnie lying next to me. I noticed Jodie leaning against a tree, watching us. I decided to go over to see her, but first I stretched out my near side foreleg, like having a good morning stretch, and gathered the energy to pick myself up. She was still standing there, so I had an all-four stretch and meandered slowly down, hoping that none of the others would beat me to her.

We stood together and had our usual silent conversation for about 20 minutes until the others felt they might be missing out on something. Boxer arrived first, but I didn't feel the urge to run away from him. Then Charlie Barnie came down; now he can be very jealous, so just as he trotted down I noticed his ear turning back. Oh, oh, I had better back off, I thought! Shortly afterwards, Ralphi followed suit. He absolutely hated to miss out on anything. Wise One was next; well everyone knows to get out of her way!

Jodie clearly didn't plan to speak to them all for long but wanted to walk with them. So, she herded Boxer and Wise One out; following suit were Charlie Barnie, Chessie, and Ralphi, and somehow I found myself in the middle of them. I didn't want to be there so I backed off and let the others carry on. Clearly they were heading up towards the gateway at the top paddock.

Now, I didn't fancy being suffocated or kicked into oblivion by Wise One as they all went through the gate, but as it turned out Wise One went through first and the others just hovered around outside. I thought if I could catch Jodie's eye she would usher them through and I could follow behind. This she very obligingly did. No one pulled any toady faces so I started through the gate. But little Ralphi was kind of blocking my path. I didn't have room to turn myself round in the gate so I just pulled my ears back and stretched my head forward to threaten him, just like he did with me on that first day I was let into this field. Well, I got the shock of my life, because he ran off! I must have succeeded in telling him off! Half of me felt a bit bad about this because he hadn't really been nasty to me since my first day in the field, but the other half of me, well, I felt quite proud. *It was the first time ever that I had plucked up the courage to tell anyone off*, apart from humans of course. It seemed as if from this day onwards he had a new respect for me.

On another afternoon when Jodie came out and played with us all, I was distinctly unimpressed. The night before I had felt Jodie was spending too much time with Chessie, my next-door neighbour. So, while Jodie was speaking to Chessie in the field that afternoon I got jealous and chased him away – by pulling the same faces that had worked with Ralphi! Actually, they may have been a bit toadier than that – I may even have shown him my teeth! I felt so chuffed, but Jodie wasn't at all impressed. Blow me, she started jumping up and down, as if to say, 'How dare you do that! That is totally beyond your limit! You do not have to go to that extreme here!'

She started to chase me away just as I had done with Chessie . I sprinted off with my head arched high and swaying from side to side so that I could see where she was running to. The easiest way of seeing her was for me to run in a big circle round her, but even although she was 15 metres away she kept pushing me away. I was tiring and slowly realised that perhaps showing my teeth and being so grumpy was not on after all. I kept running but lowering my head at each circuit, to say 'SORRY AUNTIE JODIE!' She stopped pushing me then and stood perfectly still. I thought I should maybe grovel by sidling up to her, but she still didn't move, so I very pitifully moved closer. Still no movement on her part. Oh dear, she really wasn't impressed and has truly rejected me, I thought. Perhaps I should give her a gentle nudge! And guess what? It worked!

Till this day I have never shown that kind of behaviour again. *Perhaps, if I feel someone has done me wrong, I need to learn a bit more about how to position my body rather than being so aggressive. I am still working on this, but feel I have almost cracked it. It never ceases to amaze me how humans and horses can learn so much from each other.*

FIREWORKS, FIRES, SCREAMING - MY PAST COMES TO HAUNT ME!

Little did I realise how much I had grown to rely on my new neighbours for safety.

As November started I could sense the longer dark nights, the changing moon, but it was the lack of bird song I really noticed, and the dormant grass roots. In the daytime I felt safe, but the evenings brought back memories of my past. Some nights were very calm, almost too calm, and then all of a sudden dreadful storms would throw aside whatever came in their path.

A bit like a matriarchal elephant looking after the young ones in her herd, I sensed something very strange and had a surge of anxiety for other horses. I was sure they were going to be damaged, hurt and beaten, just like I had been. I didn't know what to do. Flashbacks of bonfires and screeching from somewhere all came rushing to the fore when, nearby, fireworks started going off on Bonfire Night. These were awful memories, burning memories, cruel memories. I sweated buckets for days afterwards and was utterly exhausted from these horrific nightmares. But then I came out of my terrified state to realise that I was safe. How I so wished these nightmares would go away for ever! *Were they from a previous life or are there indeed animals hurt at this time of year, I wondered? Somehow, I just had to get through this month of November!*

Just to confirm that I am surrounded by lovely people, a 2011 calendar created by Jodie and printed by Cath and James of Bordersprint was placed in my stable and each month has a picture of an expanding me with a different person alongside – how reassuring and kind is this.

LAUDER LASS 2011 CALENDAR

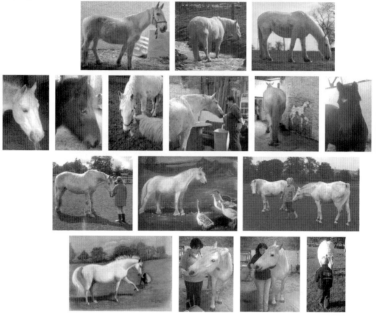

For every season there is a reason...

HOW SOME ANIMALS

AND HUMANS FEEL

I am captured on the carousel of time
I don't understand the world around me
I feel so locked in
It's as if they think I cannot see
But I see more than her or him
I just don't know how to communicate
with the world around me
I am captured on the carousel of time

I over react because I am misunderstood
My world is filled with anger and frustration
I so wish to show the world that I can be good
But the world doesn't seem to want a
    connection
I am fed up of rejection

So few people give me the time of day
Maybe one in a hundred understand me
But the others push me out of the way
How long is it going to take to make them see
I just need to be guided in the right way
I need time and the right key to unlock me
I want to feel free of this demon inside me

At long last I have found some people
Who can turn my key
I feel free of the demon
When I am with them
For the first time
I can breathe, I feel free

I have a chance to smile when I am with them
I have found what makes me happy.
For the first time ever I feel as if I am in heaven
I have laughed and smiled all day
And the devil inside me has run away

Please, come share this happy day with me
And let me show you what turns my key
I so want to stop serving the devil inside me
But I need the world to show me the way

I don't ask for much
Just a little understanding, care and attention
I am fed up of rejection

There's a lot of good inside me
But how long is it going to take
For the rest of the world to understand me
I am tired, I am weary and I need a break
The demon inside controls me
I want to break free for ever
But I need the world to help me.
So, please, watch and listen
And that will help me

Sincere appreciation is expressed to all who have helped Lauder Lass become who she is today.

Thank you for giving me a second chance...

I am one of the few lucky ones, but there are many still out there, so, when you wake up in the morning, spare a thought for those who have to go through what I had to go through.

~ *Thank you*

Chapter 29

The snowiest winter I have ever seen

'Mounds of snow'

MANY OF MY visitors came on a weekly basis until the weather made travelling impossible. So my visitors for about six weeks consisted of Jodie and some immediate locals and those who had four-wheel-drive vehicles.

I had never seen such an amount of snow as I saw this past winter. In parts it was up to my shoulders and I am 16'2"! Little Ralphi, the obnoxious Shetland pony, truly struggled to walk about, so thank goodness for being tall. But thinking about it, being small has its good points – he can get under things that I can't AND he can sneak into the feed room.

I loved going out on a crisp snowy morning, in fact my first port of call was the nearest thick white carpet for a snow-filled body bath! After rolling back and forward for about ten times I'd get up and shake it all off, finishing with a flick of my tail, and off I'd go like the speed of light, feeling totally refreshed – as a human does after having a shower.

However, there was a problem with this type of weather: as the daylight disappeared, it would become colder more quickly. I couldn't cope with a warm rug being put on my back like the others could, so at about three o'clock I would be keen to come in to my warm stable with its hay net filled and its bucket of fresh water. Sometimes when Jodie was away there were times that this wasn't possible. But one way, or another, like Wise One and Ralphi, I would always be in before the cooking smells started to waft from the kitchen. The others would come in a bit later, perhaps after Si had gone to bed!

I was still given my delicious breakfast in the morning and if the weather was really stormy we would all be given extra hay through the day. When there was a blizzard, the large cattle court doors and the ramp doors would be kept shut, making our stables draught-proof and warm. Then we would be given more hay before five o'clock and our tea would be sprinkled with garlic and molasses. The garlic made my nose run though, a bit like Jodie's nose would run after eating a hot curry! And the molasses, if I wasn't careful made my coat all sticky, but it was worth it, as was the tasty salt lick that was tied on my stable door. We would then be given more hay around midnight, so all in all we couldn't complain about this hotel for horses!

Jodie continued to give me 'Jodie Therapy'. This consisted of relaxing music in the background while she stretched my confidence to be handled. As time went on, this meant less and less bribery and corruption. To be honest, I was beginning to enjoy it but I would be quick to flick my tail or move away if I had a problem.

These 'together' moments were special and the areas she managed to get to had never been touched so tenderly before. However, as she reached new areas I could sense her despair as she discovered fresh wounds from my past.

Jodie had a wonderful way of explaining what these wounds felt like and I'd like to share it with you so that you can truly imagine what each of my scars are like. Apparently she was chopping wood 30 years ago, missed the stick but managed to skin her first finger on her left hand. To this day this wound is about an inch in length and when I touch it with my muzzle it feels like a real lump. Okay, so now that I have explained this perhaps I can share with you Jodie's findings as my confidence grew to be touched in other areas.

FIRST VISUAL SIGNS in order of discovery

1 An indentation round my neck of about four inches.
2 Clear scarring round my muzzle that initially could only be seen through binoculars, because I wouldn't allow any one to get at all close to me.
3 Two indentations on the front of my face, again that could only initially be seen through binoculars.
4 Protruding lines all the way round each hoof, each of which were ragged at the end.

FIRST WOUNDS TO BE FELT in order of findings.
MARCH 2010
A circular indentation of about an inch in depth and two inches in diameter, threequarters of the way up my neck on the off side. The four-inch indentation on my offside was confirmed by touch at this stage.

114

MAY 2010

The four-inch indentation under my jowl was confirmed and a 14-inch hard line could be felt on my offside, half-way up my stomach.

JUNE 2010

The two indentations could be felt on my face, one in line with my nearside eye, which could now be seen as more swollen than the other. The other was in line with a halter's noseband.

JULY 2010

Contact was finally made on my nearside neck, which quivered for a full half-hour, as if the nerve endings were badly damaged. All seemed to be in line with my enlarged eye and the indentation across my face. Contact here was only accepted until September when I allowed some of my 'softer' visitors to touch me there. The four-inch indentation round my neck could now be felt on my nearside as well, so clearly my batters across the face were more than apparent.

LATE AUGUST 2010

I allowed Jodie to run her hands down my offside leg, at which point she felt an indentation under my knee, and on close inspection could see the same underneath my knee on my nearside leg. A long hard scar, like Jodie's scarred finger, could also be felt all the way along the front of my chest.

Upon each of Jodie's findings I could feel her weaken; she seemed weightless, and I had the most bizarre feeling of 'I could relax a bit more' at the same time as she turned weak. This happened after each war wound was found – was she taking the pain away from me as she was desensitising them?

I still have areas that I will not allow anyone to touch, but in time I hope between Jodie and my visitors, that my still raw areas will be desensitised.

Chapter 30

Wise One's name changes to Queen Bee

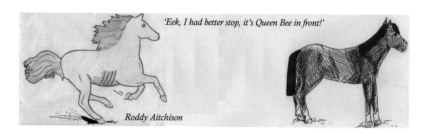

'Eek, I had better stop, it's Queen Bee in front!'

Roddy Aitchison

HAVING HAD MY behaviour brought into line by Wise One on a few occasions, I was beginning to learn how to behave when I was part of the herd. *I guess I had never been given the chance to socialise before, which is why I didn't know how to react in certain circumstances.*

I only realised how important Wise One was to me, however, at the very start of winter, when it was freezing outside and Wise One began acting in a way I had never seen before. One night, when she came into her stable, she seemed desperate to lie down. It looked as if she was in pain; her tail was swishing from side to side and her head was doing the same. Jodie stayed with her and as time wore on I could feel her becoming more and more anxious.

She didn't want Wise One to lie down – I think she thought it would make the pain worse – so she tried to keep her moving. With young Si coming out to help her, she walked Wise One round and round, just as you would a fretful baby, while Jodie kept massaging her back. What on earth could be the matter, I wondered?

They carried on like this for ages, then after several hours Jodie pulled out her little black elephant box, spoke into it and not long afterwards I heard a car pull up.

Who could it be at two o'clock in the morning? Were they coming for Wise One? Would they hurt her, or take her away? It brought back another horrible memory of a horse that died at Hob Nob's yard. Would the same happen to Wise One?

I was truly worried now, because as much as I hadn't liked her to start with, I had begun to respect Wise One more and more. These days, I saw her as my mentor. She had taught me so much in the little time I had been here and I couldn't imagine the yard without her. She was by far the most important horse here. There and then, I decided her name should be Queen Bee.

Queen Bee! I couldn't cope with the thought of losing her. She still had so much to teach me! I was so anxious for her that I couldn't eat any of my hay that night, and I couldn't sleep either. Jodie and I stayed up all night.

After a few hours Queen Bee seemed more relaxed, but it wasn't long before her pain returned, and the whole process repeated itself. A different vet came out this time and stabbed something into her neck. I wouldn't have let them do that, I thought, but Queen Bee was brave - or was it that she was in so much pain that she didn't notice the jab of the needle?

It took another two visits from the second vet over the next couple of days and I would say another two weeks on top of that before Queen Bee started to show signs of being herself. *But whatever illness she had, it obviously took its toll on her, because she seems a little more fragile these days. Perhaps that is what age does to you?*

Whichever way, she was tremendously brave, 200 times braver than I would ever have been; a perfect example of a good patient. I've put her on a pedestal and remain and always will be in awe of our 28-year-old Queen Bee.

Chapter 31

Gentle strokes turn to divine hard scratches

'A calming hand'

Judi Gunn

WATCHING AND LISTENING *are all animals' basic instincts, yours as well as mine. Mind you, from what I have seen from children's play parks I sometimes think humans lose this ability from the age of about six!* But a horse's instinct is to rely on watching and listening, which is precisely what I have been doing over the last few months. I have watched how Jodie and my visitors handle all the animals around here, including the bolshie sheep, *and really appreciate their silent but ever powerful methods of communicating.*

I have stood watching all the animals here asking for things, usually a scratch here or there. It seems that each animal, horse or dog, likes to be scratched in different places and all know precisely how to ask without kicking or shouting. It's just tremendous to see them. I often used to feel jealous of their ability and often dozed off into my deep sleep thinking of ways to pluck up the confidence to do the same, but would I ever do it?

Then one mid-February day, the weather took a turn for the better. Bulbs could be seen growing out of the ground, and the smell of people spring gardening would waft across in the warm wind. All of a sudden I felt itchy; my new summer coat was tickling through my dead winter hair roots. Was this my chance to show that I'd like some more hands-on attention? Perhaps if I wait till an evening when Jodie has more time, I could ask her in *my* way? Should I risk it though? I thought about it and decided, yes – nothing bad had happened to me since I came here.

That evening I decided to go for it. I had thought about a plan of action and decided to put it in-to practice! So, when Jodie came out on her night-time round I watched her body language for a while and just as she was about to go past me, I scratched myself against the wall where my hay net generally hung. Well, you know, she spotted my request and slowly stepped back, offering me a gentle stroke to start with. I then pushed my neck into her hand a bit more telling her, 'Harder, Auntie Jodie,' and from this point I have never looked back.

Instead of each month showing signs of improvement it is now a daily occurrence and how grateful I am. I can now cope with hard scratches on both sides of my neck, my underside and my back, all the way up to my rump. How awesome is this. *I think I am in seventh heaven.*

REFLECTION

In my stable at night I lie,
Warm and safe,
Snug and dry.
Wonder how tomorrow will be?
Friends may visit!
Treats for me!
Gentle folk who know my past
Spend time with me –
I know at last – they wish me well!
They come so near
I love it so!
I feel no fear!
No-one strikes me,
No-one shouts,
Ever gentle – there is no doubt,
My heart is full
At long last
I am ME.

Written by
L.F. The Scottish Borders

119

Fresh hay, sun shines
Cold snow, warm hugs
I'm home

This place is home
Where all is love
I'm safe, I'm home.

Written by
Penny Ryan, New Zealand

TIME WENT BY

Time went by, we have all caressed
Those scars that left you in a mess.
Your eyes are glowing like the sun
The pain is deep and always there
But now you know we are all here to care

Written by
Helen and Chloë Paterson, Edinburgh

Thank you all. Without your silent thoughts and all your patience I would never have been given the chance of this amazing feeling of being able to trust.

When things go wrong as they often do, remember all that I had to contend with but above all have patience, your time will come.

REACH FOR THE STARS

Don't give up,
Reach for the sky
Or stretch yourself
and reach for the stars
but above all
Never give up.

"Please, come share this happy day with me
And let me show you what turns my key
I so want to stop serving the devil inside me
But I need the world to show me the way
I don't ask for much,
Just a little understanding, care and attention
I am fed up of rejection.
There's a lot of good inside me
But how long is it going to take
For the rest of the world to understand me.
I am tired, I am weary and I need a break
The demon inside controls me
I want to break free for ever
But I need the world to help me.
So, please, watch and listen
And that will help me."

THANK YOU

Donna Sheep

HELPING TROUBLED HEARTS

No matter the age, No matter the issue,
Every animal and human
Is blessed with a heart,
Though often locked or hidden.
They need you to take part.

To find the key
To unlock their hearts
Please, use silence
And look within.
Above all, have patience
This is the art
Of helping troubled hearts

THANK YOU

Written on behalf of all misunderstood animals and humans
©Judi Gunn

Sarah Ryan (10).
New Zealand

Once captured but now I am free
THANK YOU ALL

If I had my way I would:

1 Insist that no offspring is taken away from its mother at an early stage, unless it is absolutely clear that they are unfit to look after them.

2 Insist that everyone experiences fun when they are growing up and are not restrained or beaten into submission.

3 Insist that everyone is brought up to accept others as equals, no matter what quality of rug/clothes or stable/house they have.

4 Insist that not only animals but humans too are given boundaries, especially at a younger age.

5 Insist that good behaviour is rewarded and consequences are given for bad behaviour; bribing with treats leads to greed, fights and misunderstandings.

6 Encourage all individuals who have the job of culling animals to do so in a humane way.

7 If someone feels something in their heart, they should go for it, believe in it and never give up.

With both animals and humans Jodie seems to actively encourage:

1 Freedom of mental/physical and visual expression

2 Spontaneous visual communication of information about experiences

3 Actions for assistance

4 Questions and clarification of answers

5 Asking for permission and assistance

6 Expression of future events

7 Pretend play

8 Requests

9 Own view point

10 Apologising

11 Respect and behavioural improvements

12 Self-awareness, motivation and imagination

13 Self-explanatory reasoning

14 Caring and respect for self, other people and animals

15 The breaking down of communication issues

16 Acceptable social interactions and social consequences

17 Planning

18 Activities created by self

19 Activities for contentment

20 The breaking down of fear barriers

21 Team building strategies

22 One hour a week of no talking

Dis-encourage

1 Being too bossy and show consequences for this trait

All of the above encourages learning problem-solving strategies

123

Postscript

In all my years of working with animals and humans I have never come across such an abused living creature. What this horse has been through is despicable but thanks to you all she has been given the chance and time to learn how to trust.

It is my sincere hope that this book will encourage others to have patience with all animals – and humans – who have some form of disability or difficulty communicating, whether it be due to **abuse, dementia, Alzheimer's, autism, ADHD, ataxia, depression or cancer. Like Lauder Lass, the feeling of rejection, uselessness or being 'labelled' that each of these individuals experience is strong and extremely debilitating:** don't let this happen to anyone you care about.

ENCOURAGE, IN A CONSISTENT MANNER

Explore with them new ways of communicating, through silence or animals or music or art, or computing. Or encourage them by singing their old favourite tunes, play them a recording of their favourite babbling brook and bird life or do something as simple as giving them a photo album or a life-size painting on a wall

All of these actions will make them feel *part* of our world to the end of their time instead of feeling as if they have been rejected from society or as if they have suffered from some form of leprosy.

Sharing someone's silent time is more powerful than feeling obliged to talk for an hour, so don't be frightened by the silence of their world. *Watch them and they will communicate with you, perhaps with something as simple as a blink of a twinkling eye – or the tap of a toe or hoof...*

Thoughts for Hooves, Paws and Hands

Teaming for a better world for animals and humans by

LETTING SILENCE SPEAK
